ED

POPCORN'S

GUIDE TO PARENT TRAINING

Omnibus Books
an imprint of Scholastic Australia Pty Ltd
(ABN 11 000 614 577)
PO Box 579, Gosford NSW 2250.
www.scholastic.com.au

Part of the Scholastic Group
Sydney · Auckland · New York · Toronto · London · Mexico City ·
New Delhi · Hong Kong · Buenos Aires · Puerto Rico

Published by Scholastic Australia in 2020.

A catalogue record for this book is available from the National Library of Australia

ISBN: 978-1-74383-402-2

Typeset in Ainslie Sans, Bizzle Chizzle, Oil Change and Slappy.

Printed in Australia by Griffin Press.

Scholastic Australia's policy, in association with Griffin Press, is to use papers that are renewable and made efficiently from wood grown in responsibly managed forests, so as to minimise its environmental footprint.

10 9 8 7 6 5 4 3 2 1 20 21 22 23 24 / 2

EDDY POPCORN'S

GUIDE TO PARENT TRAINING

Dee White

Illustrated by Benjamin Johnston

An Omnibus book from Scholastic Australia

The sun crawls across my face like a **MUTANT OCTOPUS**, its bright tentacles dragging me from sleep. I didn't plan to wake up this early, but nothing's going to bum me out today. It's the first day of the school holidays and it's full of awesome!

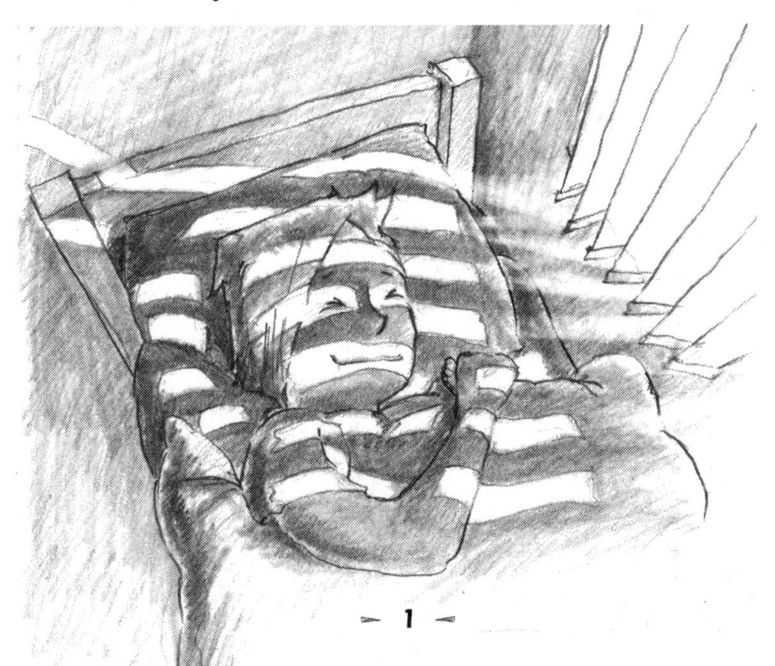

Ahead of me are 384 hours of **FREEDOM!** Beach days hanging out with my mates, Macca and Damo, racing our bikes across the sand and catching waves. No mad rush for the school bus, no teachers getting on my case and no homework. Sixteen mornings of sleeping in. And in just under two weeks, it's my birthday. Today I start the countdown. I have big plans for turning **TWELVE.**

I lean against my pillow and yawn. I could go back to sleep, but the sun and surf call me too. Hmm, what to do?

My bedroom door **BURSTS** open. It's Mum

and Dad. They're empty-handed, clearly not here to deliver breakfast in bed. Mum frowns at the trail of clothes on the floor. Dad picks up an empty Chinese takeaway container. 'Do you know **HOW LONG** these take to break down in landfill?'

Talking about food makes me hungry. I'm considering what to have for breakfast when Mum delivers the fatal blow. 'YOU'RE Grounded Edward Poppenhagen!'

My mouth opens and closes like a guppy. 'Grounded?' I gasp.

Dad nods. 'We don't like the way you're behaving lately.'

Parents always stick together. But what have I done now? I know my room's untidy, but I've seen worse. Grounding me is a bit EXTREME.

'You're not leaving this house and there will be no recreational screen time until your book reflections are done properly,' says Mum.

'But I did them already,' I groan.

'Not properly.' Dad flashes a piece of paper at me. It's a photo of a book cover reflected in our fishpond. It's a book and it's reflected! **A BOOK REFLECTION!** Great photo, even if I say so myself.

Mum takes the pic from him and shakes it at me.

'This isn't what Miss McTaggart meant and you know it.'

When I didn't get feedback from Miss McTaggart I thought she must have decided to excuse the lack of content because my photography skills are next level.

CLEARLY NOT!

'I'm very upset about this, Eddy,' Mum says.

That doesn't mean she has to go all **POLICE OFFICER** on me and ground me. Okay, so she is a police officer, but she doesn't have to bring her work home with her. I don't.

And besides, I'm the one who should be upset. It was my book that fell in the fishpond!

'Why can't we read for **FUN?**' I say. Mum should like that one. She always says that reading is stimulating and relaxing. Huh? What does that even mean?

But she doesn't look impressed. In fact, her face has gone a **PURPLISH** shade of red.

'Eddy. Analytical skills are important,' says Dad.

I know that! Mine are well developed already. **EXAMPLE:** I've concluded that there's nothing good about what's happening here. It's the first day of the school holidays, my birthday party is less than two weeks away, and Mum has decided to gaol me for who knows how long?

'Mum, it's the **HOLIDAYS.**'

'I'm fully aware of that. I'm not happy about this situation either. I wanted you to take your little brother to the beach so I could study for my criminology exam.'

'That's exactly where I was heading! I can take Davey now.' She actually studies a subject about criminals. No wonder she's straight onto me when I slip up.

Mum shakes her head. 'You're grounded until your schoolwork's done.'

'But I'm meant to meet Macca and Damo. And I have a **ZILLION** important things happening over the next two weeks.'

I wonder if that's the look Mum gives her crims. Her eyes are half-closed and her forehead is scrunched like a dried leaf. It's her 'don't **MESS** with me' look.

'You should have thought of that before you handed in those silly photos.'

I can't speak. She's serious. **I'M GROUNDED!** This is not the start to the holidays I had planned.

And what about my birthday? The invitations for my laser tag sleepover already went out.

'Doing your book reflections won't take long if you **APPLY** yourself.'

But it will now that Mum has banned screen time. That means I'll have to read the actual books – I can't even watch the movies.

Mum and Dad don't even blink at my pleading look. Well-developed analytical skills tell me that **RESISTANCE IS FUTILE.** This is a nightmare! Who knew that teachers follow up stuff on their holidays? Teachers must be like parents who clearly don't believe in holidays.

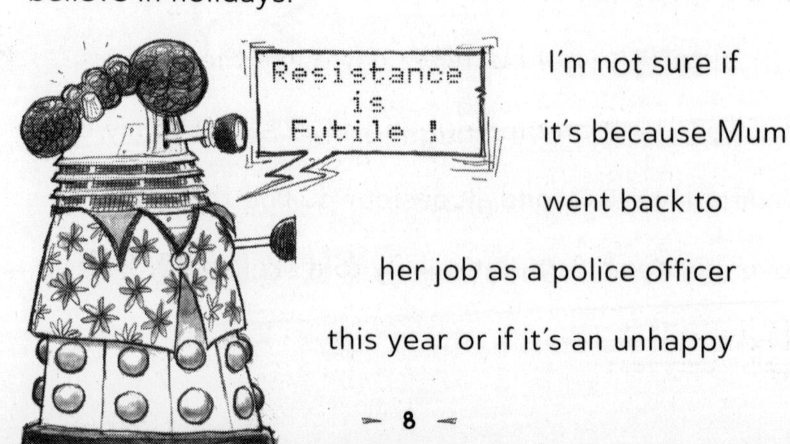

I'm not sure if it's because Mum went back to her job as a police officer this year or if it's an unhappy coincidence, but the day I got my first underarm hair, my parents turned tyrant. I mean **TY-*RANT!***

Mum took me to the shops to buy deodorant and that was the start of it. All year they've hassled about homework, the state of my bedroom, being with my mates and pretty much anything they can think of to give me a hard time about. I'm over it. Any parent who says that kids are a problem has everything the wrong way around.

'It's time to get up.' Mum navigates the clothes-trap pile I left on the floor and stands next to my bed.

For a nanosecond, I consider pulling the pillow over my head. But that's likely to make her **EVEN MADDER.**

Mum sighs as if she's the one in pain. 'The sooner you do those book reflections, the sooner you'll be free to enjoy your holidays.'

'But I don't know where the books are.'

She opens the curtains completely so the full force of the sun **BLASTS** my face.

I close my eyes. Now I know how **VAMPIRES** must feel.

She shows **NO MERCY.** 'Probably in my study. See you at breakfast.' She brushes past me and out the door.

An hour later, I'm scanning the shelves in Mum's study for book titles I recognise. Right next to one of my favourites, ***The Case of the Disappearing Rabbit,*** is a thick, creased spine that catches my eye: ***A Parents' Guide to Raising Tweens.***

I pull it off the shelf and flick through dog-eared and coffee-stained pages. It's clearly been read a **LOT.** And there's a whole chapter on grounding your child. **SERIOUSLY!?** My parents get their torture methods from a book! I quickly skim the chapter. They call grounding 'currency'. Currency is what your kid values most, like freedom. The book suggests parents can make their kids do what they want by taking away the kid's currency!

Mum and Dad have a **WHOLE MANUAL** on how to make my life miserable. Aren't there laws against this sort of thing? Shouldn't it be on a **BANNED-BOOKS LIST?**

When Dad was spreading crushed eggshells around the base of our tomato plants once, he said to me, '**KNOW YOUR ENEMY.** Snails hate crawling over these.' I pause. This book could be a great opportunity for me to get to know my enemy. I slip ***A Parents' Guide to Raising Tweens*** under my shirt, cross my arms over my chest and head to the only place I'm not likely to be interrupted while I'm reading – the toilet.

I flick through the chapters. I can't put myself through the **TORTURE** of reading every word.

A Parents' Guide to Raising Tweens could be the **MOST BORING** book ever written.

After an hour, Dad calls out, 'You okay in there?'

'Fine.'

'I have organic **PRUNES** if you need them.'

'No thanks. I'm not that hungry.'

Page by page, I tear out each chapter I've read, drop it into the toilet bowl and press **FLUSH.**

DAY 2
SUNDAY

I get woken next morning by my little brother Davey and our dog Rover playing outside my door. One of them does a **GIANT FART.** I hope it wasn't real. Davey giggles. 'You should smell this one.' No thanks. Maybe Davey has been eating Dad's organic prunes.

I wait for the air to clear before I peer outside my room. Davey is wriggling down the hallway on his stomach and Rover's copying him. I think it's a hint that they want me to hang out, but I can't. I have homework to do. I tried to forget about it yesterday, but I can't ignore the reality. The only way I'm going to escape **HOME DETENTION** is to do the book reflections the way my teacher wants. Creative thinking is not rewarded.

Davey never gets grounded, but I wouldn't want to be eight again and not allowed out without **PARENTAL SUPERVISION.** Wonder if he'll start getting the police-officer treatment when his underarm hair sprouts? Somebody should warn kids that parents who seem perfectly reasonable one day, can turn **TYRANT** the next. Luckily, kids like Davey have older brothers like me to share their wisdom.

As if on cue, Davey and Rover worm into my room.

'What ya doing?' Davey asks.

'Thinking about how to help you through the next phase of life.' Mum says that nothing prepares you for being a parent, but at least she has/had books like that most boring ever guide to raising tweens. Kids have nothing!

Suddenly my **BRAIN** starts racing. An idea is starting to form.

This idea is even more brilliant then when I caught yabbies in Macca's dam and I called mine **PAT AND LOU** because I wasn't sure whether they were boys or girls, and I brought them home and put them in our laundry sink to keep as pets. It would have been a foolproof plan except I didn't realise yabbies could climb and they found their way to the toilet. Dad got a big fright when he found them swimming around in there. Mum said that **YABBIES TASTE GREAT** in soup, but luckily Dad insisted that we return them to their natural environment.

Davey tips his head on the side and Rover copies him. 'What do you mean about helping me through the next phase of life?'

'You'll see.' My head

is **BURSTING** with ideas. I have to get them down before I forget.

I open a new document on my laptop. I have the perfect plan to help Davey and every kid out there like me who ever grew armpit hair or just grew up. Kids all over the world will be thanking me for this! **IT'S BRILLIANT!** The best idea ever! I wriggle my shoulders, limber up and start typing . . .

CHAPTER 1:

WHY I'M WRITING THIS ESSENTIAL GUIDE

I'm writing this extremely essential guide because I have to do **SOMETHING.** My parents are **OUT OF CONTROL.** They won't listen to logic or reason. They are over the top. On a daily basis, my mum and dad lose their cool and yell – I mean, seriously **YELL** – at me. Apparently, they don't like the way I'm behaving lately . . . Yeah, well, that feeling's **MUTUAL.**

It's pretty clear that Mum and Dad are out of their depth. They definitely need training on how to treat kids, and I don't mean from **ANOTHER** book written by adults. I guess raising kids isn't something that gets taught at school, but from what I saw in Mum's study, my parents **CLEARLY** read the wrong books.

They have heaps of them about '*training toddlers*' and '*raising troublesome almost-teens*'. Parents think **WE'RE** troublesome? Huh!? Have they looked in the mirror lately? What about tips for kids on **DIFFICULT PARENTS?** There's not one book out there to help us with problem parents. Not one!

And what's worse, parenting experts (NUTS*) are becoming **SQUILLIONAIRES** all over the universe by selling 'understand your kids' guides to parents like mine who are happy to **WASTE MONEY** on that kind of rubbish, but not on me.

What's so hard about **UNDERSTANDING** kids like me?

I don't like green vegetables (because I'm not a rabbit).

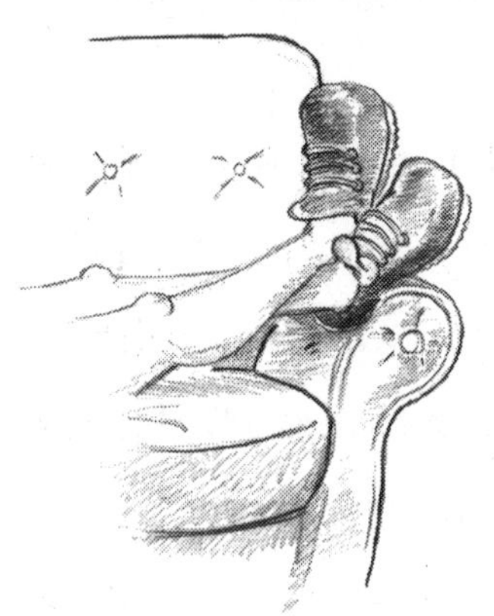

I put my shoes on the couch (because it's there).

I don't make my bed (because the pillow doesn't care if the sheet ends up on the floor).

SIMPLE!

Parents, like my mum and dad on the other hand, can be weird, daggy and mean. They're so complicated. **EXAMPLE:** grounding me for the holidays. I mean, seriously, who does that (besides a police officer practising her incarceration skills)?

Parents seem to **THRIVE** on making life difficult and embarrassing for kids.

Take my last name **'POPPENHAGEN'**, for example. The Poppenhagen name has been around for more than **ONE HUNDRED YEARS,** but do you think anyone can say or spell it properly? Oh no. Imagine trying to write Edward Poppenhagen on your preschool paintings. No wonder I started calling myself **EDDY POPCORN.** I'm legally changing my name when I'm older.

Now you can see why you must read this **ESSENTIAL GUIDE.**

Keep my **GUIDE TO PARENT TRAINING** under your pillow, in your sock drawer or under your smelly sneakers – somewhere safe where siblings won't steal it. (They will definitely want to.)

DISCLAIMER: I've conducted extensive research (spoken to at least **TWO** kids and a parrot) to bring you this important information. All examples are based on real events and no names have been changed to protect anyone. If you try my methods and they don't work, **PLEASE DON'T SUE ME.** Sue my parents, the Poppenhagens, instead.

IMPORTANT NOTE: This book is NFP (NOT FOR PARENTS). It contains material they may find offensive and, quite frankly, they don't need to know about.

***WARNING:** This book contains traces of NUTS. Many parenting experts are known as NUTS (Not Unlike Tomato Sandwiches) because they're hard and crusty on the outside and soggy in the middle.

DAY 3
MONDAY

Next morning, the **DING** of my phone wakes me up. There's a message from Macca.

Where have you been? Wanna meet me and Damo at the beach in an hour?

I WISH!

My phone dings again. The other message is from Damo, wanting to know when I'm coming to the beach.

Can't. Grounded. I message back.

That sucks!

That mean no Game of Drones? asks Damo. *I got to level 14 yesterday.*

CRUEL. He's ahead of me now. And by the time these reflections are finished and I'm allowed to play again, I'll be even further behind.

Onya, Damo. I text back. I'm genuinely happy for him. Not so much for me. *Gotta go.* I don't want to know what fun Macca and Damo are having without me.

In spite of the fact that everyone in my class and probably the **WHOLE SCHOOL** (except for Davey who's stuck here with me) is out enjoying the surf and sun, Mum shows **NO MERCY.**

At breakfast, she asks, 'How are the book reflections going?'

Groan. 'Great,' I lie because of course they're not. They're not going anywhere. I've been working on something way more important, something to change the **DESTINIES** of kids everywhere . . .

'I can't do the second reflection,' I say. She doesn't need to know that I haven't done the first one either.

She sighs. 'Why not?'

'Um . . . the book fell in the . . . err . . . fishpond.'

'How?'

'You don't want to know,' I mumble.

Mum has X-RAY hearing. 'Yes, I do.'

'It was an accident.'

'Of course it was.'

She pulls her credit card from her purse, a highly unusual action. 'I don't want to see you grounded for the entire holidays so I'll pay for a new book. Make sure this one doesn't end up in the FISHPOND.'

'Gee thanks, Mum.' She could just unground me then none of this would be an issue.

'Don't leave your homework till the last minute. You don't want me to **CANCEL** your birthday party as well.'

OMG! I will *not* let *that* happen! The only one positive about this whole situation is that Mum's giving me heaps to write about in my parent training guide.

HORRID HOMEWORK AKA WEEKLY TORTURE

Whoever invented homework must have been pooped-on-by-a-bird, liked being bossy or hated the thought of kids having fun. (Must have been a **PARENT.**)

Don't you hate the way parents nag you about homework? If they're so interested in your homework, why don't they do it **THEMSELVES** – and save you the trouble?

'Don't leave it to the last minute,' they tell you.

WHY NOT? How many times have they waited till the day before someone's party to **FINALLY** tell you that you're allowed to go? (And by then it's too late to buy anything cool to wear.)

And let's face it, finishing your homework on the bus isn't last minute! It takes some people an hour or more to get to school. And as for grounding kids who don't do their homework, that can cause lifelong **TRAUMA**. It's a well-known fact. Ask any kid.

It's also a known fact that teachers give out **TOO MUCH** homework. Everybody knows it, even the teachers. My parents won't listen when I try to point this out to them. I mean, why give kids two book reflections when **ONE** would be more than enough?

And even though they can see it causes me mental and emotional stress, my parents would **NEVER** write a letter excusing me from doing homework. When it comes to homework, parents and teachers seem to share the **SAME BRAIN**.

Once I told Mum and Dad, 'I'm sick of homework. I don't think I'll do any tonight.'*

*__WARNING:__ I don't recommend this. Dad did the eyeball bulge and Mum frothed at the mouth. I shouldn't have been **THAT** honest with them. It scored me double homework and no screen time for the next week.

EDDY'S HELPFUL HOMEWORK ANTIDOTE

Luckily for you, I've thought up some **ANTIDOTES** that will help you in this difficult situation.

1. The best way to stop parents nagging about homework, is to nag **THEM** for help. If you nag enough, they might even **DO SOME** for you.
2. Also, make sure any homework you do is 'seen'. Leave your homework books or laptop on the dining table. It helps create the **IMPRESSION** that you've done a lot more homework than you actually have.

3. Homework can be used as an excuse to get out of **BORING JOBS** around the house that you're expected to do with a smile. (Even though Mum and Dad whinge every time they have to clean the oven – which **THEY** dirtied in the first place.)*

***WARNING:** This last plan isn't foolproof, especially if your homework is overdue. (SEE how honest and helpful I am? I hope you remember this when you're writing your **REVIEW** of my book.)

Two chapters of my parent training guide done already. At this rate, the **WHOLE BOOK** will be written by the end of the holidays.

Dad wanders into my room as I'm tossing around ideas for chapter three. He's home from work already. I can't believe the whole day has **GONE BY.**

'How was your day?' he asks.

'Awesome!' Being grounded is so much fun. **NOT!**

Dad picks up the Chinese takeaway container and shakes his head. I can feel another enviro lecture coming on, but instead he turns his attention to my room.

'It's an absolute **PIGSTY** in here. And it reeks like a garbage tip.'

Geez. He really knows how to make a person feel good. As if being grounded isn't bad enough?

'You can't possibly concentrate, working in this mess.'

I *can't concentrate* while he's here, that's for sure. I **LEAP** out of my chair. 'I'll clean my room now. But I could use some help.' That should give him the hint to leave. Especially since I have new inspiration that I need to write down before I forget.

'Sorry, Eddy. Your room, your responsibility.' Still clutching the takeaway container, he hurries out the door.

MISSION ACCOMPLISHED!

CHAPTER 3:

YOU THINK MY ROOM'S A MESS? HAVE YOU LOOKED IN THE GARAGE LATELY?

My room is kind of messy, but calling it a **PIGSTY** is way harsh. Parents should take a roll around in their own pigsties. Our garage, for example, is full of junk that Dad plans to **REPURPOSE** because he doesn't want it going into landfill. The back corner is piled high with stinky organic compost and manure to keep it safe from **POO-EATING** Rover. But do I complain that my bike smells like poo because of all Dad's stinky gardening stuff? **COURSE NOT!**

To prove my point about the pigsty garage, I sneak out of my room and do an actual stocktake. This is what I find:

GARAGE CONTENTS

(FIRST TEN THINGS LISTED)

I could have filled up this whole book listing what was in that garage so I decided to keep it to ten things.

1. **A PARROT.** (Sorry, he came with me to do the research. Guess I can't count him.)
1. One complete electric push mower and a mower that doesn't work anymore (minus wheels).
2. Old computers (2) and old televisions (2).
3. Mushroom-growing kits (5). (Nobody, even a mushroom lover like Dad, could ever eat that much fungus).
4. Box of high school musical **COSTUMES.** (It's hard to believe Mum could have worn them all. Especially when they're so weird. There's an **INFLATABLE** flamingo costume, an avocado and a chickpea. I wonder if that's what she was wearing when she met Dad. He loves **CHICKPEAS.** Mum must have been an imposter before she became a police

officer. That would explain all these costumes because she can't even sing.)

5. Three-person tent (3) and two-person tent (4). (Enough tents already. How many tents does one family need? **WE'VE NEVER EVEN GONE CAMPING**!)
6. Thirty-two empty cardboard boxes that Dad plans to repurpose. (He made me a **CARDBOARD GUITAR** once, but I could never get it to make any sound. And he built Rover a cardboard dog kennel for inside, but Rover chewed it up.)
7. Stacks of wire coat hangers that Dad plans to make into light shades.
8. A bag of cloth **NAPPIES**.
9. A jolly jumper (That thing parents use to hang babies from doorways. I don't remember it, but Mum and Dad say I used to think it was fun.)
10. Broken bird cage. Dad used the back and one side to train his tomato plants up.

Obviously the garage is the **REAL** pigsty, so why do Mum and Dad (the custodians of the garage) feel they have the right to yell at **ME** to 'Clean up your bedroom'?

EDDY'S BIZARRE BEDROOM ANTIDOTE

The only way to stop parents nagging about cleaning up your room is to keep them out of it **ALTOGETHER.** Once, I pushed my bookcase **AGAINST** the door so they couldn't see inside my room. (The only problem was that I couldn't get in or out myself without climbing through the window . . . and this aroused **SUSPICION.** In fact, a neighbour thought I was a burglar and called the **POLICE,** causing all sorts of issues because Mum was one of the officers on duty that night.)

Another option is to distract them by messing up other parts of the house with finger painting or **GRAFFITI,**

or bringing Dad's mushroom farms in from the garage because they looked lonely. This tactic will distract parents from going near your room often enough to realise it's starting to look like the inside of a **NUCLEAR MELTDOWN**.

If all else fails, open the garage roller doors and put up a **GARAGE SALE** sign in your front yard. This method has a number of benefits.

1. It points out to Mum and Dad the double standards of asking you to clean **YOUR** room when **THEIR** garage is messier.
2. When they see what's in the garage they will be compelled to go exploring and finding their way out through the maze of mess could

take some time. By then, you'll be **LONG GONE** . . . to a mate's house where, hopefully, their mum won't yell at you because mums seem to yell mostly at their own kids.

3. They'll be so distracted by all the people at the garage sale that they'll **FORGET** about you and your room.
4. You could make extra money helping Mum and Dad at the garage sale because, as I will probably discuss at some point in this **EPICALLY** helpful guide, your pocket money isn't enough to keep a rabbit in lettuce. (By that I mean that you don't earn enough pocket money to buy lettuce for your rabbit. I'm not suggesting that you literally **'KEEP'** it in lettuce. Rabbits live in hutches. Everyone knows that. Whoever heard of keeping a rabbit in lettuce? They'd eat their way out.)

DAY 4
TUESDAY

I'm about to start work on my parent training guide when there's a **KNOCK** on the front door. I hurry down the hallway, optimism in every stride. It could be Macca or Damo come to campaign for my **FREEDOM.**

It's not! Standing on the front step is my nemesis Steve with his little sister Jen. I bet Steve has never been grounded in his life. He's the kid that everyone thinks is perfect. The one that makes parents and teachers say, 'I wish you were **MORE LIKE** Steve.'

(I do not wish I were more like Steve. Life as **EDDY POPCORN** is way more fun, unless you're grounded, of course.)

'Brought Jen over to play with Davey,' he says.

That's a **RELIEF.** It would be worse if Steve had come over to hang out with me. But that would never happen. Steve and his friends are all 'A students'.

'How have your holidays been?' he asks politely.

'Awesome!' I lie. 'How's the **BOG?'** I ask. 'I mean, the blog?'

Steve is monitor for our class blog. Miss McTaggart goes through the share drive and picks out the best work and

Steve uploads it to the blog. I would not want to be **'BOG MONITOR',** but Steve seems to think it's important. He tells kids they have to be nice to him or they won't get their work on the bog. As if anyone would care! My stuff has never been shared on the class bog and I'm pretty happy to keep it that way.

I grin at Jen who's holding her pillow and sleeping bag tight. 'I'll let Davey know you're here. I think he's out the back with Rover.'

'I'll pick her up tomorrow afternoon,' says Steve as Jen walks inside.

'Okay.' I know it's rude, but I don't invite him in. I guess it's not his fault, but I don't want Mum having '**PERFECTION**' to compare me with.

I close the front door before he can ask me anything awkward like, 'Why are you spending this incredibly sunny and awesome fourth day of the school holidays inside instead of at the beach?'

Jen dumps her stuff and races out into the backyard with Davey and Rover. **LUCKY THEM.** It's so unfair that Davey gets to hang with his friends while I have to do homework.

And even worse, if Steve 'bog monitor' finds out that I've been **GROUNDED,** he won't let me live it down. Now might be a good time to start those book reflections so I can get out of prison before he finds out. Luckily, I started reading one of the books yesterday and it didn't take that long to finish. Well, I did read it late into the night. **YAWN.** Miss McTaggart said we can use whatever medium we want, so I go for the quickest option. I set up my microphone, sit directly in front of my computer and press **RECORD.**

EDDY POPPENHAGEN'S BOOK REFLECTION №1

THE SCIENTRIFFIC ADVENTURES OF ALBERT STEIN

My dad was rapt when he saw me reading this book. I think he still hopes that I'll follow his dream and become a **MUSHROOM SCIENTIST.**

But the whole point of the story is that **ALBERT I N STEIN** doesn't want to be a scientist like his parents. His dad does genetic research and is trying to find out how to stop people getting old. His mum is a mushroom scientist, a mycologist. Dad almost went **PURPLE** with excitement when I told him that.

Al has to hand in his science project or he's not allowed to go on school camp. I can totally relate. Parents use blackmail on their kids all the time. **EXAMPLE:** I'm not allowed to hang at the beach with my friends until I finish my book reflections.

Even though his parents would like him to do his science project on old age or mushrooms, Al thinks that would be **BORING.** (I don't blame him.) He wants a pet (just like me), so he decides to do his project about how rats live and he buys one so he can observe it. Al's mum is away at a mushroom scientist's convention, so Al just needs to keep his new pet **RATTUS HOUDINI** away from Dad who doesn't like rats even though he has them in his laboratory.

Al thinks that if he looks after Rattus well and shows how responsible he can be, that he might be allowed to keep his pet. Sounds like a good plan to me. I might have to try it.

I liked **THE SCIENTRIFFIC ADVENTURES OF ALBERT STEIN** because Al was funny and his life was a lot like mine. If you want to know whether he gets to keep his rat, you'll have to **READ THE BOOK.**

Phew! I press **STOP.** That was exhausting. I can't stop yawning and my eyelids are fluttering when Mum strolls in carrying a basket of folded washing. 'Make sure you put these away properly in your drawer.'

'Yes, Mum.' I yawn again.

'I hope you weren't gaming on your computer

last night, Eddy. You know screen time is

BANNED.'

'I know.' I hold up ***The Scientriffic Adventures of Albert Stein.*** 'I was reading this for my book reflections.'

'Oh. Well, if you'd done that homework last term **LIKE EVERYONE ELSE**, you wouldn't be stuck here doing it now.'

If I had parents who didn't **TORTURE** their kids I wouldn't be here now! Then again, I'm not sure that such a parent actually exists.

Which brings me to my next chapter.

CHAPTER 4:

A HOLIDAY IS SUPPOSED TO BE A HOLIDAY NOT HOLIDAYS FROM HELL

Somebody needs to tell Mum and Dad what the word **'HOLIDAY'** actually means. A 'holiday' is a time of recreation and rest. It's not supposed to be an opportunity to do useless book reflections.

When I was little, my parents tried to get me to sleep all the time – said I needed it to grow. Boy that changed. Now they **KICK** me out of bed early on school holidays and even wake me up when I'm about to take a nap. Don't parents realise how dangerous their behaviour is? I could be having a **GROWTH SPURT** at any moment.

A TRUE SNIPPET

Eddy stayed up late one night watching old *Doctor Who* episodes. If Eddy hadn't watched the episode, he would never have known how dangerous Daleks can be – potentially **LIFESAVING** information.

So, next time your parents catch you having a well-deserved midday **NAP** and complain that you stayed up late, you can tell them you were watching something **EDUCATIONAL** and that screen time teaches you all sorts of vital things.

EDDY'S HELPFUL HOLIDAY ANTIDOTE
Here are some of my methods to increase sleep quota on school holidays.
1. Hide under the blankets, lying as flat as you can, so your parents don't realise you're there.
2. Tell them to come back later. You're busy growing.
3. Explain the definition of 'holiday' to them, and suggest that they might like to consider taking one too.
4. Make a wish list for your parents of dream holidays you can all go on.

Sometimes **MIRACLES** happen in families. When Dad gets home from work, Mum says, 'Why don't you take Eddy out to get some fish and chips? He could do with the fresh air. He worked all day on his book reflections.'

Maybe she feels bad about wrongfully accusing me of staying up late playing **COMPUTER GAMES.**

Dad grins. 'Interesting book he was reading yesterday.'

Don't get any ideas, Dad. I am not going to be a mushroom scientist. Still, getting out of the house and having fish and chips for dinner is a double bonus, so I grin and say, 'Yeah, it was.'

Minutes later, we pull out of our driveway and I watch in horror as Dad's index finger/prime picker goes **UP HIS NOSE** and rotates inside his nostril. Dad complains that my room looks like a pigsty but some of *his* habits really gross me out, especially when he does them in **PUBLIC.** Nose picking is first on the list. Dad doesn't care when or where he picks his nose or who watches.

He takes a short break to turn a corner, but when we stop at the traffic lights, his finger goes halfway up his nose again. As if that's not bad enough, I look across and see Steve and Jen in the car next to me, **WATCHING.**

And of course, they're heading to the same fish and chip shop we are. I mean it's great to see them and everything, but while Dad's ordering our food, Steve points to a jar of **PICKLES** on the counter and says, 'Did they come out of your dad's nose?'

CHAPTER 5:

NOSE PICKING – IT CAN HAPPEN ANYWHERE

Why do dads, in particular, pick their noses in public? I mean, let's face it, most days you find them almost up to their **ELBOW** in nostril. Have they ever thought about using a tissue or their sleeve?

And they pick **EVERYWHERE!** In the car, at the doctors – in public – **AAAGH!**

As if this isn't bad enough, sometimes you

have to pick the boogers off the remote control before you use it.

EDDY'S NEAT NOSE-PICKING ANTIDOTE

Aside from carrying a bucket around in case this gross sight makes you want to **VOMIT**, you could try these other anti-nose-picking remedies:

1. Pretend to pick your own nose and wipe it on your brother. Dad will be so busy telling you off that he'll forget what he was doing. (This isn't **FOOLPROOF** because it doesn't matter what he's doing, Dad will go back to picking his nose.)
2. Watch a 'Save the Planet' documentary with him. (Some sacrifices are worth it.) Don't let him out of your sight and gently remove his hand when it goes **ANYWHERE** near his face. Do this for about forty years and he might eventually kick the habit.
3. Probably the most effective remedy is to dip his hand in **DOG FOOD** when he's not looking. That way, he'll be reluctant to let his

fingers anywhere near his nose. (Canned dog food is especially good because it gets under the fingernails and the awful smell lingers for ages.)

4. Some medical experts suggest that nose picking is a nervous condition and Dad needs to **RELAX.** (Oh, pleeeease. He nods off in front of the television after he has picked his nose all the time. If he were any more chilled, he'd be a block of ice.) Anyway, if you think your dad suffers from stress, enrol him in meditation, **YOGA** or aerobics classes. YOUR DAD WILL LOVE YOU FOR IT!

FINGER-PICKING DETERENT DIPS

STINKY-DIP

When his fingers stink this bad, there's no way he will want to stick that up his nose

SPICY-DIP

Trust me...if you use this dip you'll know about it if his finger ventures up his nostril....Ouch.

VISIBLE-DIP

If you use this dip, then **EVERYONE** is going to know just where his finger has been.

DAY 5
WEDNESDAY

Last night I ate so much fish and chips that I wake up feeling like a python who swallowed a crocodile, so I decide to skip breakfast.

TODAY'S FOCUS: my bid for freedom! One book reflection down, one to go. I slap on my clothes from yesterday and sit down at my computer.

That reminds me, I forgot to buy that new copy of the book that fell in the **FISHPOND.** I'll do it now. I reach into my jeans pocket for Mum's credit card.

It's not there.

It's not there!?

I feel **SICK.** I've lost Mum's credit card!

I glance around my 'busy' room. It could be

anywhere. **ANYWHERE!** What was I wearing when she gave it to me? Oh yeah, these jeans!

There's only one thing for it. My only course of action is likely to be a parent pleaser, but desperate times call for desperate measures. **CLEANING** your room is a form of child torture that seems to have been around forever.

To help alleviate the boredom, I put my music on full throttle and start with the pile of clothes on the floor next to my bed. Somewhere underneath all this is a washing basket. I burrow my way in and extract it. Ewww, those socks are definitely overdue for a wash.

I turn the washing basket right way up, roll a dirty shirt into a ball, take aim like a league player and shoot.

'YES!' The shirt goes in first time. This is the perfect opportunity to improve my basketball skills. Timing and accuracy is everything.

I pick up a pair of shorts and score again. I'm **GOOD** at this.

Unfortunately, Mum doesn't seem to appreciate my talent/room-tidying activities. She **BANGS** on the door. 'Eddy, keep the noise down!'

It's not noise, **IT'S MUSIC!** I'm a kid. I need entertainment.

CHAPTER 6:

KIDS NEED ENTERTAINMENT AND PARENTS DON'T GET IT

'Why do you have the music up so **LOUD?'** Dad asks.

'Because I'm listening to it,' seems like a reasonable response, but not to parents. We

have to put up with them making us do boring things, like cleaning our rooms, so the least they can do is put up with our music, which shouldn't be a problem because our taste is **AWESOME.** Choosing your own music is every kid's right. Here are my tips for maintaining yours.

1. Turn your music down, then **GRADUALLY** turn it back up again. If you do it slowly your mum won't even notice.
2. Text a friend or family member who talks a lot and tell them, Mum/Dad needs a chat. When they ring, your mum or dad will want to take their conversation somewhere **PRIVATE** so you'll be free to keep listening to your music. (If you're lucky like me and you have a dad who spends a lot of time outside talking to his organic vegetables about making a better world, then you might only have one parent to worry about.)
3. Give the lyrics of your favourite songs to Mum and Dad. If your parents are **'SINGERS'**, and most are, they will learn every word and sing along with your music. This will be ugly

at first, but they won't be able to tell you to turn the music off because they'll be singing along to it themselves. Also, they will lose their voice soon from too much singing.

4. Don't bother trying the 'I need loud music and more fun' argument because, as everyone knows, 'fun' is not a **PRIORITY** for parents. They seem to drop it from their vocabulary the day you're born.

Another chapter down, I go back to tidying my room. If I don't find Mum's credit card, I might never see the outside world again. I tip the dirty clothes back onto the floor then pick them up piece-by-piece and carry out a new **THREE-STEP** plan I devised:

1. Check the pockets.
2. Shake the clothing out.

3. Do the sniff test. If it doesn't smell, it goes into a cupboard or drawer. If it does, it goes into the washing basket. (Ew! I think a possum must have **DIED** in my second-favourite pair of jeans. They are definitely due for a wash.)

Two hours later, I can see parts of the floor, but still no credit card. This is a **DISASTER.**

I lift up the rug that I forgot I owned because it was under the dirty-clothes mountain. No credit card! I pull my sheets off and remake my bed for the first time in ages. No credit card! I empty out my schoolbag and find an apple from last term. It's starting to look like one of Dad's fungi. My room is unrecognisable. That's the good part! The bad part is that I **STILL** haven't found Mum's credit card.

Stomach churning, I knock on her study door.

'Come in.' Mum turns around, her nose screwed

up and her forehead wrinkled, but I don't think it's because of me for a change. She's been reading a boring-looking book called ***Crime and Criminology.***

'Eddy, just the person I want to see.'

I bet I know exactly what she wants. I feel sick.

Then I see it on her desk. **WHAT?** Did I give it back to her? Great! I cleaned my room for **NOTHING!**

Mum holds up her credit card. 'I grabbed this off your desk last night to buy more research materials. This studying is killing me and the bank balance. So many books to buy.'

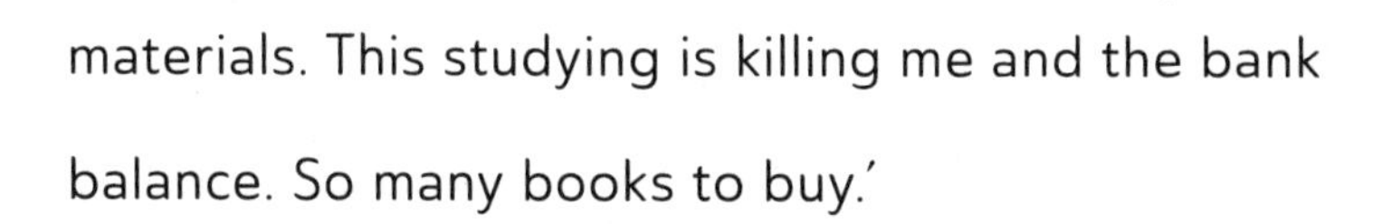

If she's expecting sympathy, it won't come from me. She should try living on my **MEASLY** pocket money.

'You bought that book, didn't you, Eddy?'

Hmm! No! 'Um, I haven't had time.'

She hands me the credit card. 'Order it now before you forget. And give the card straight back to me.' She laughs. 'I'd hate you to **LOSE IT**.'

Me too! 'I cleaned my room,' I say.

'That's great. I'll come and look.' She stands up. 'We can chat on the way.'

FANTASTIC! 'Sure.'

Mum peers into my room. 'Wow, Eddy, this looks so much better. Well done.'

'Thanks.'

She puts a hand on my shoulder. 'I've been studying so hard, I feel like I've neglected Davey and Jen. Perhaps you could take a break from your homework and hang out with them for a bit. I still have work to do.'

SO DO I!

'They're in the backyard. I think they're playing dress-ups with Rover.'

So they're probably doing fine without me. 'Great.'

'Thanks, Eddy.'

I log into the online store, key in the book title and add it to my shopping cart. An ad for the ***Game of Drones*** accelerator app also pops up on my screen. It includes two special fighter drones. Cruelly tempting!

I hesitate for a second. But **ONLY** a second. It doesn't cost much and I can pay Mum back with the birthday money I get from Grandma. Grandma always gives birthday money. Anyway, as soon as I've finished the book reflections, I'll be allowed to play the game again. Plus, if Mum had told me she took back her card, I wouldn't have **WASTED** all that time cleaning my room.

I add the app to my shopping cart and proceed to the checkout.

Even after I buy the book, I'm feeling pretty good, until I realise that I should have ordered an ebook. The print one is going to take at least two days to get here . . . two extra days grounded . . . two extra days not hanging out at the beach with my mates . . . two extra days **NOT** playing ***Game of Drones*** . . .

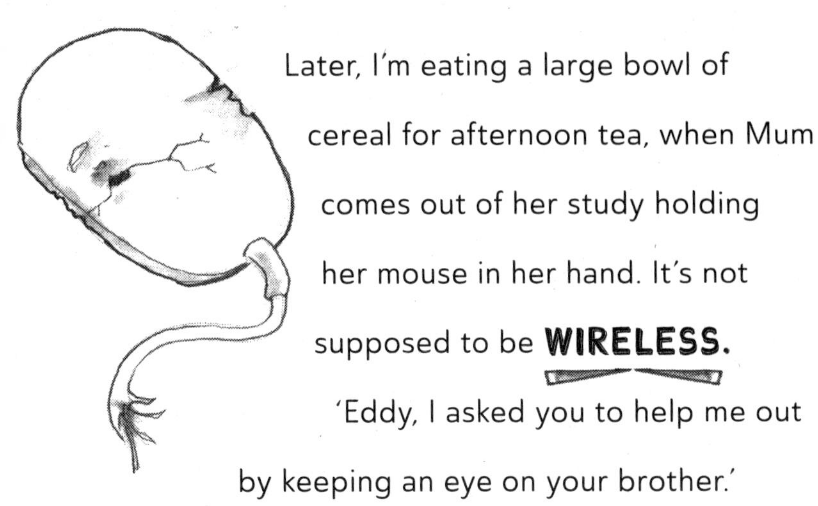

Later, I'm eating a large bowl of cereal for afternoon tea, when Mum comes out of her study holding her mouse in her hand. It's not supposed to be **WIRELESS.**

'Eddy, I asked you to help me out by keeping an eye on your brother.'

'Davey chewed that? He must be having a growth spurt.' I try to hide my grin.

'Of course he didn't. It was Rover.'

I glare at our dog and he grins back. 'I don't even know **HOW** Rover got inside.'

At the sound of his name, Rover tries to jump on my lap. My cereal goes flying and milk spills all over the tablecloth.

'Quick. Wipe it before it **STAINS.**' Mum thrusts a cloth at me.

I finish cleaning and the doorbell rings. Steve's here to pick up Jen. Awesome! Being grounded means your enemies are allowed to visit, but not your friends.

'Hello, Mrs Poppenhagen.' Steve walks in and smiles at Mum. She grins back as if he's some sort of **GENIUS**, probably because he's the only one outside the family who can say our last name right.

'How are you, Steve?' Mum holds the chewed mouse behind her back.

I grab Rover by the collar and try to drag him into the backyard. He doesn't budge.

'I'm very well, thank you, Mrs Poppenhagen.' Steve says Mum's name again as if he's trying to **PROVE** that the first time wasn't a fluke.

Mum glances from Steve to me and back again. 'Perhaps you'd like to come to Eddy's twelfth birthday.' She beams at Steve.

WHAT THE . . .?

'But I'm grounded, Mum.'

I can see by Steve's grin that I've given him too much information. By tomorrow all the kids from school will know that Eddy Popcorn has been

Mum shakes her head. 'Of course you're having a birthday. We've already booked the laser tag and sent out invitations for your sleepover.'

Great! Now Steve knows all the details of my private life . . . including the fact that I'm having a sleepover. At least he doesn't know about my **GUIDE TO PARENT TRAINING**. Steve would probably side with the parents. He's pretty tall for his age. Who knows? He could even be a parent in **DISGUISE.**

'Laser tag. Awesome! I'd love to come,' says Steve.

'Great!' My birthday is **RUINED** before it even happened. I can't believe Mum invited someone I don't even like to *my* birthday. Total **NIGHTMARE.** There must be something I can do about it!

DAY 6 THURSDAY

ZIT is a small word for a big ugly thing. One appeared on my cheek without warning last night and this morning it has multiplied and merged into a huge weird lump. A whole **FAMILY** of zits is making a takeover bid for my face.

I'd hide away in my room all day only hunger calls. I **CREEP** into the kitchen with my head averted, but Mum is onto it straightaway. As she places yummy-looking poached eggs on toast on the table, she kindly reassures me that alien zit is so small, people will hardly notice.

Then Dad wanders in. He stares at me, points and guffaws. 'What's that **GIGANTIC** thing on your face?'

He ignores Mum's warning glare and peers **CLOSER.** 'I'm sure I never had a growth like that when I was your age. Must be all the **CHEMICALS** we're ingesting these days.'

I've lost my appetite and storm off to my room (in a dignified way of course). I think about whether to hide my head in a pillowcase. Then again, I could stick **DAD'S HEAD** in a pillowcase instead. But that's not the solution I recommend. I think there are laws against it.

CHAPTER 7:

ZITS ARE TAKING OVER YOUR FACE AND DAD WON'T IGNORE THEM

EXPERTS say that drinking less milk will reduce the number of zits you get, but if that means giving up chocolate, **FORGET IT.** There has to be a better way to avoid zits and Dad's unwanted feedback.

You don't want to **MORTALLY** wound Dad, but if you scare him just a bit while he's shaving and he nicks himself and has to wear a bandaid, it will help him understand what it's like to go around with a blob on your face and have people **COMMENT** on it.

Being the kind and mature person you are, though, you may prefer a different solution. After all, you're not trying to cause Dad pain, you just want to help him **EMPATHISE** with your predicament.

EDDY'S ZANY ZIT ANTIDOTE*

If empathy encouragement doesn't work, try Dad distraction. It's easy.

If distracting Dad doesn't work, stay **OUT** of the kitchen until he leaves for work.

Unfortunately, this made me miss the school bus once and a long walk on a cold morning with a sore face is **UGLY**.

***WARNING:** Don't try this on mums.

HOW TO DISTRACT DAD LIST

WARNING: This is not something to try on Mums, but Dads are easily distracted. Here are just a few things you could try.

1. Give Dad something else to look at besides the zit on your face.
   Buy a rubber cat poo or vomit from the joke shop and place it on the bench where Dad makes his breakfast. Now he'll be thinking about his stomach, not your zits.
2. Drop your school report on the table in front of him (warning: this could lead to a whole new set of problems).
3. Sing your Dad's football team's theme song as loud as you can. He's bound to join in and forget all about your zit.
4. Burn the toast.
5. Tap on the window to make the dog bark.
6. Tell Dad there's someone at the front door to see him. If he falls for this one, now's your chance to make a quick getaway.

ALTERNATIVE ANTIDOTE: MUMMIFICATION

In spite of how it sounds, this has nothing to do with your mum. Wrap a bandage around your face and tell Dad you're a **MUMMY** in the school play about ancient Egypt. He's bound to believe you. My dad did. Parents are susceptible to believing things that they think will **IMPROVE** your report card.

Evading Dad's zit commentary at breakfast was a higher **PRIORITY** than the soft poached eggs on crunchy toast I left behind. Now I'm not so sure I had my priorities right. My stomach growls to show me how much it **DISAGREES** with my decision.

To distract myself, I scroll through texts from Macca and Damo, full of surf reports, ***Game of Drones*** updates and bragging about all the cool stuff they're doing on *their* school holidays. I bet they don't have **MONSTER ZITS** invading their faces.

What's happening with your birthday, Popsicle? asks Damo.

Yeah, turning twelve is an important occasion, texts Macca.

Don't think they'll let me do anything. I hate lying to my mates, but I still haven't worked out what to do about Mum's birthday invite to Steve. I'm not taking him to laser tag . . . or anywhere! And I definitely **DON'T** want him sleeping over.

But what about laser tag? texts Damo.

Mum cancelled. Another lie.

So unfair! How come you're still grounded? asks Macca.

Haven't you done those book reflections yet? asks Damo.

It's complicated.

No it's not. I got mine online, says Damo. *It's easy. You type the name of the book into your browser and all these reviews come up.*

I never thought of getting book reflections off the **INTERNET**. It would be the easiest and quickest way, especially now that my book will take another day to get here. But I'm a writer now and I have standards. I can't **STEAL** someone else's work! That would be cheating, like parents copying child-torture ideas from books like ***Raising Tweens***.

All this thinking makes my head ache. And now my stomach's rumbling like a jumbo jet. Seems like pretty good timing when Mum calls out, 'Lunch is ready.'

That's until we sit down at the table and she serves up multigrain **LIVERWURST** sandwiches.

Davey and I screw our faces up at each other. Even worse than the standard Liver*worst!* Liverwurst sandwiches on multigrain! Why would you put seeds that look like **RAT POO** into perfectly good bread? And liverwurst tastes every bit as bad as it sounds. This has to be child cruelty.

I've been hungry a lot and Mum says I'm growing like a weed, but liverwurst is *not* the kind of food I want to subject my tastebuds to. I **BRACE** myself. This will be a challenge – maybe even harder than writing book reflections.

Mum seems to mistake my **HORROR** for admiration. She winks. 'We need to feed that brain of

yours. A growing kid like you needs his iron.'

Double groan. 'Davey needs it more than me.'

'And he's eating his sandwich.'

When Mum goes to get water, Davey pretend **VOMITS** at me across the table. Half his poo sandwich is already gone.

Mum's back at the table, devouring hers fast, as if it's chocolate, as if it actually tastes good. I wince as I watch the rat-poo seeds disappear into her mouth.

I chew each mouthful slowly and try not to gag. Finally, my plate's empty except for the crusts.

Mum's onto it. 'You didn't eat your crusts.' She leans over and pats my head. 'Eat them up, Eddy. Crusts make your hair **CURL.**'

'Yeah, Eddy. Crusts make your hair curl.' Davy mimics. His plate's empty and he's already loading it into the dishwasher.

Somehow, I finish the crusts without vomiting and Mum grins at me **SMUGLY.** As if I'll be forever in her debt for her making me such a bountiful feast. Where do mums get these weird ideas?

She takes my empty plate. **'WANT MORE?'**

I almost **REGURGITATE** the last mouthful of rat-poo sandwich. A shake of the head is the best I can manage.

CHAPTER 8:

WHY WOULD YOU EAT THAT? FOODS THAT MAKE YOU PUKE

It's like some sort of test. Stuff **REVOLTING** things into your kid's stomach to see if it **BREAKS** them. Parents have even been known to boast

to other parents how their 'not fussy' kid will eat *anything*. **NOT NORMAL!** I mean, liver and kidneys – we already have them, so why would we want to eat someone else's? I hate to dwell on mushrooms, but they just keep cropping up. If I were meant to eat dirt, I would have been born a **WORM**, wouldn't I? And what about steak – it's so **CHEWY**. If I wanted to exercise my jaws, I'd talk more or eat more **LOLLIES**.

So why are my parents so bossy when it comes to food? Why do they tell me vegies are good for me when everyone knows they're grown in the **DIRT?** Yuk! How can that be good for you?

WHY ARE PARENTS SO BOSSY WHEN IT COMES TO FOOD?
1. Because they can be.
2. They like to be bossy about everything.
3. Food can't fight back.
4. It's payback for when they were a kid.
5. If you don't eat you'll die, so this is blackmail

EDDY'S FABULOUS FOOD ANTIDOTE

Some food, like multigrain liverwurst sandwiches, tastes so **AWFUL** that the dog would rather eat cardboard than the 'scraps' I try to feed him under the table. Clearly they

must be a favourite food of Mum's because she serves them up **ALL THE TIME.** When that happens, try these ideas.

1. At mealtimes, tell Mum you'd love one of her **SPECIAL** lemon drinks. Mums love it when you ask for anything fruit related. While she's in the kitchen, slip a sandwich onto her plate. She'll probably think she **FORGOT** it was there. Mums worry about their memories a

lot so she might be too embarrassed to say anything.

2. **COMPLAIN** about the food so much that you get sent to your room and don't have to eat it. The risk here is that it might get served up **COLD** to you at the next meal. If you're lucky, you might find a half-eaten peanut butter sandwich or apple in your schoolbag. Even stale food can be better than liverwurst sandwiches.
3. Offer to **PAY** a sibling to eat it. This only works if you get a decent amount of pocket money, which **I DON'T**.

DID YOU KNOW?

When mothers become **PREGNANT**, hormones are released into their body. (Of course you knew that. Everybody does.)

It's a known fact (you know it from reading this book) that word patterns are released into mums' **BRAINS** at the same time as the hormones. That's what makes them say (over and over) things like 'Crusts will make your hair curl' (as if everyone wants curly hair) and 'Carrots are good for your eyesight'. (Admittedly, I've never seen a rabbit with **GLASSES** – but what does that prove?)

It's even possible that this behaviour in parents is because they were **PROGRAMMED** by *their* parents. (It's a scary thought and it could happen to you one day – **UNLESS YOU READ THIS BOOK FROM COVER TO COVER.**) Just sayin'.

DAY 7 FRIDAY

I've been on holidays for **A WEEK** and still haven't seen the beach. A whole week and I'm still grounded. That's why my **PARENT TRAINING GUIDE** is so important. I have to save other kids from the same fate.

I'm bracing myself for another day of extreme torture when the doorbell rings. I hope it's not Steve. I don't want to see him again and I certainly don't want him meeting **MONSTER ZIT.**

'Can you get that, Eddy?' Mum calls out.

In spite of the fact that they're not supposed to be here, Macca and Damo have come to rescue me! And, like **TRUE FRIENDS,** they don't even mention the temporary growth on my face.

Mum appears in the hallway.

'Hi, guys. How are you enjoying the holidays?'

Does she have to **RUB IT IN?**

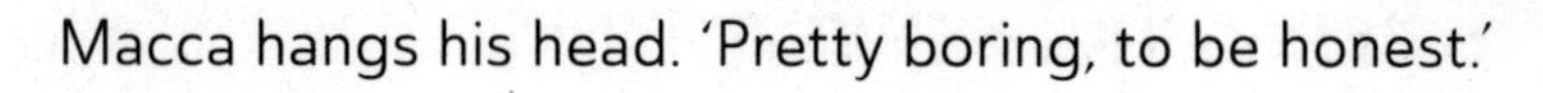

Macca hangs his head. 'Pretty boring, to be honest.'

Damo nods. 'Yeah. Not hanging out with Eddy sucks.'

NICE ONE, guys.

Unfortunately, Mum doesn't budge. 'That's too bad, but Eddy knows the rules. He has to finish his homework . . .'

'Couldn't you break the rules just once?' Macca grins. 'I break them all the time.'

I wish. Macca clearly doesn't know what it's like to have a mum who's a police officer. She never breaks rules.

Mum puts on her fish-pout face. 'Parents set boundaries for a reason.'

Yeah, to **TORTURE** their kids.

Mum walks them out as if she's worried they might turn back and **KIDNAP** me.

Mum and Dad say that rules are for my own good, but I can't see how spending my holidays grounded is of **PERSONAL BENEFIT.**

CHAPTER 9:

RULES AND BOUNDARIES

To train a parent, you have to understand that they are an **ALIEN RACE.** They don't think like you do. In fact, there's scientific evidence to suggest that parents are more like **SQUIRRELS** than people, which is probably why they don't seem human when it comes to setting rules that make no sense and **ENFORCING** them.

Just like squirrels, who make their own laws

when it comes to stealing and hoarding stuff, parents can change rules and boundaries to suit **THEMSELVES!** Example: ever noticed how parents keep a close eye on the clock when it comes to your gaming time, but there's no time limit on **CHORES?** Parents are quite happy for you to spend all day helping them in the garden, the kitchen or around the house.

Dad's claim that 'The lawn won't take long', can turn into **TWO HOURS** of raking, composting and digging a new garden bed. My tip is to get the dog to help, but to be honest, he mightn't be that useful. Dogs are great at digging, but **NOT** where you want them to!

WHY PARENTS ARE LIKE SQUIRRELS:

- They like to hoard (that's why the car doesn't fit in the garage)
- They eat anything that's put in front of them (even Brussels sprouts)
- They make a clicking sound with their tongue when they're agitated (especially after they've just read your report card)
- They're always renovating their homes.

ALTERNATIVE ANTIDOTE:

RADICAL RULE REMEDIES

I have some great tips on how to make rules and boundaries work for **YOU**.

1. If you're asked to help with the chores and your parent indicates a timeframe, set every alarm you have to go off at **ONCE** when the time is up. Even if the chore is only half done, the alarms are your signal to walk off the job. If your parent complains, ask for more **GAMING TIME** as a trade-off for more work. This will show parents how little you can actually do when your gaming time is limited.
2. Negotiate an agreement where every chore completed scores **A LATER BEDTIME**. If your parents are like mine and have huge to-do lists, you could be allowed to stay up after **MIDNIGHT!**
3. Parents worry about your health, so don't be afraid to play the 'sore knee' or 'twisted ankle' card. You can claim a headache

too, but I generally don't recommend this as parents are likely to blame screen glare and **BAN YOUR DEVICES.**

I start munching an apple, lamenting the fact that Damo and Macca's attempt to break me out of here has **FAILED.** Rules and laws are supposed to protect us, but I don't need protecting. The beach would not become dangerous just because I went there when I'd been grounded. It's a rule that Mum and Dad could **BREAK** without causing any physical harm to me.

See what I mean? Rules and boundaries are set by parents to get us to do what they want us to. That's **CONTROL,** not protection. It's a typical example of parents' control-freakish behaviour.

CHAPTER 10:

PARENTS ARE CONTROL FREAKS

Mum and Dad want control over everything. My birthday, my **LIFE**, my holidays, my homework and my brain. My parents do and say what suits them – so why can't I?

When I want to go out with friends, they complain about me being out so much and want me to spend time at home.

Then Mum pulls out the **'FRESH AIR'** card when she wants me to stop playing computer games. Which is weird because all Dad talks about is how polluted

the world is, but imagine how much pollution must come just from the **FARTS** of the dogs in your street? Of course the air at the beach is

always fresh and good for you. That's why it's **MIND-BLOWING** that a parent would stop you from going there for any reason.

I'm almost a teenager, a few short years off **ADULTHOOD.** Yet Mum and Dad get to choose what I eat, where I live, what school I go to, when I'm allowed to hang out with my friends, when I go to bed at night – even who to **INVITE** to my own birthday party!

How come **THEY** get to decide everything?

Writing *EDDY POPCORN'S GUIDE TO PARENT TRAINING* has made me realise how ingrained their control-freakish behaviour is.

Mums and dads say they 'know best' and no amount of **EVIDENCE** seems to convince them otherwise. They dish out control-freakish punishments that could result in lifelong **TRAUMA** for kids.

Like the time Davey and I fought over Rover when he first came to live with us. Davey put **DOG POO** in my room to make me not like Rover, and I put dog food in his **SANDWICH.** Mum was 'very disappointed with both of us'. Her punishment of choice was to send us to our rooms, which I wasn't happy about, seeing as mine **STANK** of poo.

Dad had a 'better idea'. He said we had to 'learn to be kind to each other', so he sewed a huge t-shirt out of potato sacks and we had to wear it together. My arm went through the right sleeve and Davey's arm stuck out the left one. Mum painted **BROTHERS ALWAYS SHARE** on the front. We had to wear it for a whole day and it was a nightmare. At one point Davey tried to run away from me and tripped, and we both fell over and landed in a pile of **CHICKEN MANURE.** Rover came and licked it all up, and when he vomited all over us, we discovered that eating poo made him **SICK.**

EDDY'S CLEVER CURE FOR CONTROL-FREAKISH PARENTS!

Control-freakish parents are clearly a serious problem for kids. **LUCKILY,** I have some excellent tips to help you deal with them.

1. Allergies are a good way to avoid things that control-freakish parents want you to do, but you have to be **CONVINCING.** Practise

sneezing in front of a mirror. Then tell Mum and Dad you have a **SEVERE ALLERGY** to mushroom harvesting, cleaning the kitchen or whatever awful job they want you to do. Prove it by presenting your perfect sneeze. It also helps to carry half an **ONION** in your pocket to make your eyes water. The downside is that you will end up smelling like a **HAMBURGER**, but it's a small price to pay.

2. Agree to what they want but say you'll do it later. Parents are **NOTORIOUSLY** forgetful because they have very busy and important lives.
3. **SELECTIVE HEARING** is another method that parents use all the time. They hear you being mean to your brother, but they never hear what he said to you **FIRST**. Parents are also selective when it comes to the things that you want or don't want. **EXAMPLE:** they never seem to hear when you say, 'I've had enough liverwurst sandwiches and organic fish this week, so perhaps we could have

chocolate pizza for dinner instead.' Even if they do hear it, they don't seem to pay attention to your suggestions, so don't feel **OBLIGED** to respond eagerly to every word that comes out of *their* mouth. So, use selective hearing on **THEM.** If they tell you 'Go and tidy your room', tell yourself that they actually said, 'Go and chill out on the computer in your room'. It doesn't quite sound the same, but it's **CLOSE ENOUGH.**

Look out for more excellent tips in *EDDY POPCORN'S GUIDE TO PARENT TRAINING*. If you think this is another example of being told what to do, then don't feel compelled to read on. It's your **CHOICE.**

But don't say I didn't warn you. If you don't devour and digest my words of **WISDOM,** you might not **SURVIVE** the humiliation caused by your weird and embarrassing parents.

And even worse, you may end up **LIKE THEM.**

My book arrived **LATE** yesterday so I've spent a boringly long day reading, but by dinnertime, I still have a third left to go and the whole reflection to write.

All afternoon, amazing smells have been coming from the kitchen. Dad's cooked his specialty: organic roast chicken and berry cheesecake for dessert.

YUM!

'This is lovely,' says Mum, when it's ready. 'The chicken is cooked perfectly.'

'Thanks, Dad. I agree.' I **HIGH-FIVE** him.

'Me too,' says Davey.

Dad grins. 'Aww thanks, guys. Nice to have my

hard work appreciated. Who wants dessert?'

'Me!' we all say at once.

After my **SECOND** helping, I'm feeling pretty full and ready to chill out and finish reading my book.

Dad takes my empty plate and passes it to Mum who's loading the dishwasher. 'We've hardly seen each other these holidays, Eddy,' he says.

He puts an arm around my shoulder. 'Let's watch TV together. We haven't done that for ages. There's a great documentary on tonight about saving the bees. It's one of my **FAVOURITES.**'

I love honey and I'm all for saving bees, but this wasn't what I had planned. 'But I have a book reflection to do.'

'It can wait till **TOMORROW,**' says Dad. 'Come on! It's the weekend.'

He looks so eager and that meal was amazing. I can't disappoint him. I flop down on the couch next to him and get myself comfy. Dad's got himself in prime position. He picks up the remote control and I brace myself.

CHAPTER 11:

TAKING CONTROL OF THE REMOTE CONTROL

Even though they have control over **EVERY** aspect of your life (see previous chapter about control freaks), parents want to take charge of the **TV REMOTE** as well.

It's totally unfair that you don't even get to choose something as small as what television program to watch. And it's totally bizarre that parents don't trust your impeccable taste.

EDDY'S RADICAL REMOTE CONTROL ANTIDOTE

Mums aren't usually such a problem when it comes to remote controls, but dads have a vice-like grip. **FORTUNATELY,** all parents are prone to falling asleep in front of the television so that's your chance to take control. Unfortunately, dads also have the uncanny ability to **WAKE UP** as soon as the television channel is changed. So

if Dad is one of those, it might be best to let him keep sleeping and sneak away.

But if you want to **RISK** it, here are some great tips on taking control of the remote control.

1. Try **HIDING** it. Dad will soon tire of getting up to change channels manually, so he'll probably move on to another screen in the house with an accessible remote control. (Encourage him to watch the **DODGY** television in the kitchen.) If you plan to take control of the television, it might as well be the **BEST ONE**.
2. Save up for **YEARS** and buy a television for your bedroom. (As if you're **EVER** going to have enough money for that with the pitiful allowance you get!)
3. Relocate one of the televisions to **YOUR** room. Mum and Dad aren't likely to notice it there. They won't be able to get through the door for starters (especially if you pushed your **BOOKCASE** against it).*

***WARNING:** This plan isn't completely foolproof because if the doorway is blocked, you'll have to get the television into your bedroom through the **WINDOW.** But if you're like me, you enjoy a challenge. And if it means getting control of at least one thing in your life, it's worth the effort.

When I can't stand any more of Dad's **REMOTE-CONTROLLING** ways, I sneak off to my room and check my messages. There's one from Damo. *Hey Popcorn, you still popped?*

I message back. Haha. *If you mean grounded, yeah I am.*

Come on, man! They can't ground you for the whole holidays. It's your birthday in a week.

He's right and I'm getting kind of **DESPERATE.** Even if I finish my book reflections, laser tag and a sleepover involving Steve 'bog monitor' is not what I had planned.

CANCELLING my birthday isn't an option. I refuse to stay eleven forever.

I've been so busy writing **EDDY POPCORN'S GUIDE TO PARENT TRAINING** (which, as you can see from my experiences, is sorely needed), looking after Davey and bonding with Dad that I haven't had a

CHANCE to finish my book reflections.

And I won't get much done tomorrow because I have a FOOTBALL game, the last one for the season. It's my get-out-of-jail-free card, but I'd much rather be surfing.

DAY 9
SUNDAY

Even though I'm still grounded, Mum and Dad decide to let me play football this week because the team is one player short, it's the last game of the season and they think it's **UNFAIR** if I let the rest of the team down. They don't seem to have any reservations about being unfair to me, though.

I plan to sleep in the car on the way, but Davey's poking his **ELBOW** into my ribs because Rover's spread across the other half of the seat and Davey is squished up against me.

Meanwhile, Dad's in a joking mood. **GROAN!** He pulls away from the kerb, putting his foot on and off the clutch so that the car hops like a kangaroo.

Davey's tennis racquet flies into the air and hits my head. **WHACK!**

'Thanks, Dad.' The racquet hit so hard it made my eyes water.

'Sorry,' says Davey.

'Not your fault.' I look out the window, trying not to show how much it hurt.

Great! Steve 'bog monitor' just passed us in his dad's car, grinning. I bet he saw everything.

'You're so **EMBARRASSING,** Dad,' I say.

Dad kangaroo hops even more. The thing that worries me the most is that he might stall the car and not get it going again. Our family car runs like a **THREE-LEGGED** dog with asthma. Dad bought the car from the guy across the road when he was towing it to the tip because Dad hates stuff going to landfill. He took it to the mechanic who lives behind us and paid her *'Whatever it takes to get it running'*. Mum refuses to spend any more money on the car, and it's still not really running – not properly. And now Dad's 'funny kangaroo hops' make it shudder and rattle even **WORSE.**

By the time we get to the football ground, I feel like I've been shaken around in a washing machine.

CHAPTER 12:

CAR CATASTROPHES

Being seen out in public with your parents in their daggy car is probably one of the worst **HUMILIATIONS** a kid can suffer. You shouldn't have to tolerate their weird driving as well. Next time you're in the car and Dad does something embarrassing, like play a game of kangaroo hopping, threaten to **JUMP** in the driver's seat and show him how a kangaroo really hops. Seeing as you've never **DRIVEN** a car before, that should be easy.

EDDY'S FAMILY CAR CRISIS ANTIDOTE

My parents seem to think that when I'm trapped in the family car with either or both of them, it's a great **OPPORTUNITY** to 'chat'.

Research shows (well, there has to be some

explanation for this weird and annoying behaviour), that parents actually do embarrassing driving and other weird things in the car to **BOND** with you. They believe that doing something 'funny' will make you laugh. (It would if it **WAS** funny).

Parents also assume that if they act like a child, you will be impressed. Seriously, only an adult could think of a theory like that. Whatever you do, don't humour them by **LAUGHING**. It only makes them worse. Try these things instead.

1. Distract them by shouting, **'DOG FART'**, and winding down the window. This usually works best if the dog is actually in the car at the time.
2. Better still, try not to get in the car with them in the **FIRST PLACE**.
3. If you're like me and your family car is a **WRECK**, obviously you won't be able to buy a new car with your weekly allowance, but you don't have to put up with the embarrassment of your old one. **WALK** everywhere you can!

4. If you are forced to travel in the family car, always carry sunglasses and a wig or some other form of **DISGUISE.**

CAR TRIP DISGUISES

"THE ELVIS"

"THE BEATLES"

"THE ELTON"

(Come to think of it, this might attract more attention that you really want)

At the football, everything is going great until I trip over the other team's ruckman and crash to the ground. I twist my ankle and can't get up. As if that's not bad enough, a free kick is awarded **AGAINST** me for pushing the other player in the back.

I try to get to my feet

and take my place on the field.

Unfortunately, Dad doesn't accept the umpire's decision. He's winding up and his face has gone all **SPLOTCHY!** 'You've got to be joking!' he screams in a voice that would deafen an elephant.

By now, everyone is staring at him.

'Were you even watching the game?' he yells at the umpire.

Davey grabs Dad's arm and tries to pull him away from the other parents and players, but Dad's not budging. He's made it his **MISSION** to tell everyone that I should have a free kick instead of a penalty. Even if he's right, I don't think that the twenty parents he told agree with him, especially seeing as they're from the other team.

Coach Finley helps me to the bench and I lie there with my eyes closed, trying to pretend this isn't happening.

As if this isn't embarrassing enough, Mum rushes over and flings her arms around me, **CRYING.** 'My poor darling,' she sobs. I'd get up and run away, only my ankle hurts too much.

Even Davey's finding this a bit much and he crawls **UNDER** the bench.

I decide at that moment that I will never play sport again.

CHAPTER 13:

WHEN YOUR PARENTS ARE BAD SPORTS

I found this profound quote somewhere. I'm not sure what it means but I thought it could be passed on to mums and dads everywhere who throw **TANTRUMS** on the sports field.

Parents who behave like drop kicks at the footy are totally missing the point.

NOT HELPFUL?

EDDY'S SENSATIONAL SPORT ANTIDOTE

Here's how to escape the pain and **HUMILIATION** of parents at sporting events.

1. Hide the sports fixture and tell your parents that the match is **ACROSS TOWN** (somewhere at least sixty kilometres away) and that the coach wants to drive you. By the time Mum and Dad get back from the wrong venue,

the game will be **OVER.** (If you're lucky, they will have done the grossery shopping on the way home.) Now that is definitely a win-win situation.

2. Try the **AMY BALL METHOD.** This is an interesting case study on how a sporting career can flourish without parental interference. (Brought to you specially by *EDDY POPCORN'S GUIDE TO PARENT TRAINING* – feel free to write and thank me.)

AMY BALL'S STORY: A CASE STUDY

Amy Ball was the goal shooter for a very **FAMOUS** netball team. (I can't tell you which one because I might get sued.)

Her mum and dad went to **EVERY** match. When Amy got ready to shoot a goal, they'd yell out, 'Go, Aim!'

Each time she went for goal, her parents yelled out, 'Go, Aim!', and Amy found herself dropping the ball, **LITERALLY.**

As her form went bad, so did sponsorship deals with dog-grooming franchises and goat's-cheese manufacturers. Amy had to do something before her whole career **CURDLED.**

One day, she was letting the chooks out to peck at stuff and she accidentally came up with the perfect solution. Amy discovered that if she **LOCKED** her parents in the chook shed, it stopped them from going to the game and being annoying.

Without her parents yelling encouragement, Amy Ball soon became a **WORLD CHAMPION.***

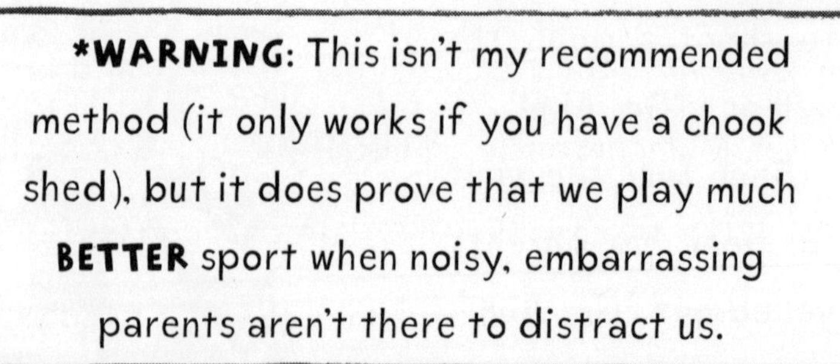

***WARNING**: This isn't my recommended method (it only works if you have a chook shed), but it does prove that we play much **BETTER** sport when noisy, embarrassing parents aren't there to distract us.

Rattling along in the family car makes my ankle hurt worse and by the time I get home, I'm not feeling like doing my book reflections. Mum helps me **LIMP** inside to the couch and put my leg up. She even hands me the remote control, which I hide behind my back in case Dad sees it and decides to try another father-and-son **BONDING SESSION.**

'Did Dad tell you what we planned for tomorrow?' asks Mum.

I'd planned to finish my book reflections. 'No.'

'He has the morning off work, so I've booked us in for our family **PORTRAIT.** Won't that be fun?'

About as much fun as sleeping on a **BARBED-WIRE FENCE!** (Not that I've ever done that or would recommend it.)

'But, Mum, my ankle's **SORE.'**

She pats my shoulder. 'It will probably be fine by then, and anyway, you'll be sitting down for the photos.'

I knew the family portrait fiasco was coming, but we usually get more warning. Grandma always visits for my birthday and that's when she gets presented with the latest family photo of the four of us grinning hideously. The timing this year is bad on so many levels. It's not just the fact that I had planned to finish my book reflections. It's also going to be hard to hide the new family of **ZITS** that recently took up residence on my face. I do not want them to star in this year's family portrait.

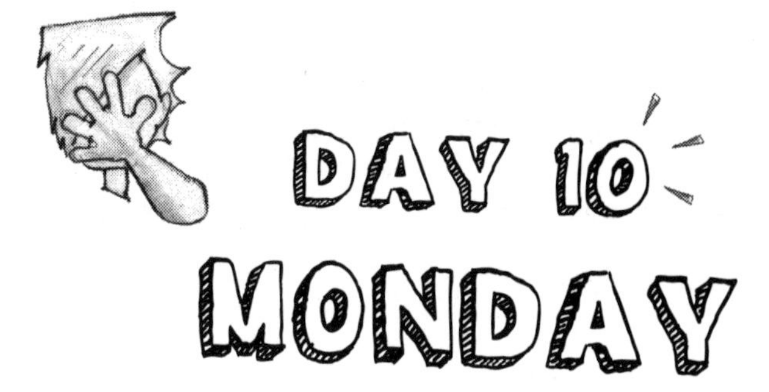

DAY 10 MONDAY

My head starts to ache as soon as I wake up and remember what's on for today. No matter how **AWFUL** this family portrait turns out, a copy is bound to end up on our lounge room wall for everyone to see. And in spite of what Mum claims, having our photo taken won't be fun!

Even though it's probably **FUTILE**, I spend the whole bumpy car ride to the studio trying to work out how to get out of this.

Photographers are child torturers too. They know that we hate having our photos taken, but they do it anyway. Must be because our parents pay them to. Some people will do anything for money.

'Come in. Come in.' Bart, our usual photographer, grins at us like a **SPIDER** inviting a fly into its web.

Our photography appointment is for an hour, but I know from past experience that this nightmare will last way longer. My ankle is still sore from football, but I try not to limp. I don't want this guy asking details about my private life.

Dad's wearing the wrong tie, **AGAIN.** Luckily Mum brought the 'right' one with her. But by the time they've 'discussed the issue' and agreed to Mum's terms, half a yawning hour has passed. Eventually, Mum turns her focus on me and notices the rips in my shirt.

'Eddy, you could have taken more care getting dressed.'

I did. I took care to make sure that this year's family portrait would be more **VISUALLY INTERESTING.** By now nobody feels like smiling (not that Davey and I ever did). The photographer tries to get us to say 'Cheese' or 'Bananas' and other stupid things that wouldn't even make a kookaburra laugh. He clicks away as if it's the most fun he's had in ages. He mustn't get out much.

CHAPTER 14:

FAMILY PHOTO FIASCO

You all look like **ZOMBIES:** fake grins and staring eyes. The photographer's still not satisfied and insists you do it again and again while he blinds you with glaring lights and his **ULTRA-WHITE** teeth.

Mum and Dad will still think these terrible pictures are **FANTASTIC** and buy five of them, even though you only have one grandma. And the extras will get displayed all over the house for your friends, and enemies like Steve **'BOG MONITOR'**, to see. You can't let that happen.

EDDY'S FANTASTIC FAMILY PHOTO ANTIDOTE

Your reputation depends on getting out of family photos full stop or going **INCOGNITO**.

Here's how:

1. The stomach ache is a good excuse, but if you use it too often, Mum and Dad are likely to cart you off to a **SURGEON** for exploratory surgery. Not nice. And you won't avoid it because they'll book the family portrait for **ANOTHER** day (after the exploratory surgery).

2. A less painful option is to get a friend to **PUNCH** you in the eye so you have to wear sunglasses. Now nobody will recognise you when the picture is hanging on your lounge room wall or posted to your parents' social media. At the last minute, you could also slip in those **VAMPIRE FANGS** from the joke shop. The photographer (who may have got his teeth from there too) will be so thrilled everyone is **FINALLY** smiling that he probably won't notice your disguise.

ALTERNATIVE ANTIDOTE— LETTER TO GRANDMA

If I have advance **WARNING** about the impending photo shoot, I write a letter to Grandma and try to talk her out of the whole family portrait idea.

Grandma **LOVES** receiving letters, but she hardly ever gets them anymore because normal people communicate by emails, text messages and **FACEBOOK**. (Can you believe Grandma's allowed to use it but you're not?) Now the only thing delivered to Grandma's letterbox is junk mail and bills. She's always thrilled to receive a letter from a **BELOVED** grandchild.

EXTRA TIP: Use spellcheck. Grandma will be right onto any spelling mistakes.

SAMPLE LETTER TO GRANDMA

Dear Grandma

I am very concerned about the future of the ***WORLD*** *and that's why I think that getting our photo taken again is a bad idea.*

It's such a waste of the earth's ***RESOURCES*** *and we will need all these things to get our photo taken:*

- *new clothes*
- *new shoes*
- *hair combs*
- *hair gel*
- *nose-hair remover for Dad*
- *petrol to drive to the photographers*

- *a new car to drive to the photographers*
- *the camera the photographer uses*
- *picture frames for the photos.*

*It will also cause **POLLUTION** and be a waste of money. (Grandma will particularly love this last part. Grandma loves it when you are **'SENSIBLE'** with money.)*

So, although I'd love a new family photo too, it would be better for the world if we didn't get one. I'll tell Mum and Dad to call the whole thing off, shall I?

Your loving grandchild

etc.

How could Grandma **NOT** love a letter like that? My extra tip is to use big writing and stretch the letter out to three pages. Grandmas love getting long letters.

(See how **HELPFUL** I am? So many great suggestions for you to try! I hope you'll remember how helpful I've been when you are writing your five-star **REVIEW** for this excellent book.)

Somehow, I survive the family portrait session – just. On the way home, we stop for lunch and, apparently, Mum needs to do some shopping. GROAN. Normally she'd drag us around with her, but seeing as I have a sore ankle, we get a reprieve and she drops us at Gr8 Games. I find a copy of a new game called ***Boy vs World*** that everyone has been talking about at school.

I'm studying the game's technical details when Dad wanders over. 'Phew, glad that family photo **SAGA** is over,' he says.

'Yeah.' Maybe Dad and I have something in COMMON.

'What you got there, buddy?' he asks.

Bonding is one of the things parents use to justify family photo torture. Time to capitalise. 'You'd love this game, Dad. We could play it **TOGETHER.**"

'Looks interesting.'

'Can I get it?' I ask. Surely he can do this one thing for me – after I made the supreme sacrifice for Grandma.

He checks the rating. 'Seems suitable.'

FIRST hurdle overcome.

'Can you lend me the money, Dad?'

Mum arrives just as he's considering my very reasonable request. Talk about bad timing.

Dad shakes his head. 'You need to learn to **SAVE** your money to buy the things you want.'

That's a joke. The amount of pocket money I get,

I'd have to save for the next ten years to afford this game – well maybe not that long – but with all the stuff I do, like having a family portrait taken for Grandma, my allowance is pathetic. Sometimes I even take the rubbish bins out. I seriously need a **RAISE.**

DAY 11
TUESDAY

Davey's at Jens house and Dad's gone to the office, so it's just me, Mum and Rover. I can hear Mum rushing around the house getting ready for Grandma's visit for my birthday. Visitor equals family cleaning **FRENZY.** Dad was up vacuuming at six o'clock before work . . . thanks for the early wake-up. Yawn. No wonder I'm still tired.

I'm in my room at my computer, hoping Mum forgets about me. Rover is lying next to me on the **RUG.** I think he was pleasantly surprised to find it after I did the clean-up.

'Eddy, can you wipe and mop your bathroom, please?' Mum calls out.

Groan. I was hoping she'd forget I was here. 'Sore ankle,' I claim.

'It looked like fine when you were walking around Gr8 Games yesterday.'

'I'm doing homework.'

'I'm a bit under the pump. I'll **DOUBLE** your pocket money.' Mum stands in the doorway. 'You've done a great job with your bedroom.' It could be a compliment to encourage me to help her with the cleaning, but my room actually does look quite good. I've set my desk up with my laptop and some books . . . like a **REAL** writer.

Doubling my pocket money is a bit too good to refuse. 'I'll finish this and I'll be right there,' I say.

'Thanks, Eddy. That's great.'

After she leaves, I wish I'd asked for **TRIPLE.**

CHAPTER 15:

PATHETIC POCKET MONEY THAT WOULDN'T BUY ENOUGH TO FEED A RABBIT

Practically **EVERYBODY** I know gets more pocket money than me.

And my parents aren't sympathetic. Sometimes, it's hard to understand how family finances work. Dad gets enough money for his organic manure and mushroom farms. Then there are Mum's books and singing lessons (although she forgets to go). Yet they expect me to get the most out of life on a **MEASLY** ten dollars a week. See how well they'd survive on such a pathetic allowance.

I've tried to get them to see this issue my way. They respond with things like, 'I only got **SEVEN** cents a week when I was your age'. (As if anyone would believe that.) When they told me that one, I had to resist the urge to show surprise that money was actually invented back then.

*Translates as: I see you have washed the dishes, fed the budgie, mowed the lawn put out the garbage and walked the dog. Here are two bushels of wheat

A QUOTE FROM SOMEONE FAMOUS

Giving kids ***MORE*** *pocket money helps them develop independence and a sense of responsibility.*

I actually made this quote up, but that's between us, **RIGHT?** Sounds like something someone who's NUTS would say, don't you think? (If you've forgotten what NUTS means, see my glossary at the back of my amazingly **INFORMATIVE** book.)

EDDY'S MARVELLOUS MONEY ANTIDOTE

If all attempts to get a pocket money raise have proved futile, I've found there's only one thing to do. Rent yourself out as a **'HOME HELPER'** and offer to clean the car for ten bucks. Parents hate cleaning cars so they're **GUARANTEED** to say 'Yes' to this one. Next, get your little brother/sister to clean the car for two bucks and everyone's happy. Mum and Dad have a clean car, your sibling thinks they're **RICH** and you've made an eight-dollar profit. (Nice going.) If you're an only child, **BAD LUCK**.

While I'm cleaning the bathroom, Rover runs past carrying my new book. I wrestle it out of his mouth, but the damage is already done. He's taken quite a few chunks out and the rest of the pages are stuck together with dog **SLIME.**

When I tell Mum, she says, 'You should take better care of your things.'

'But I was cleaning the bathroom.'

Mum **SHRUGS.** She's not helping.

A taxi pulls up outside and Grandma walks inside.

'Hi, Grandma,' I say.

She squeezes me in a huge Grandma hug. 'Look at you, Eddy. So big now!'

I hug her back. That's when it **HITS** me. Grandma is here for my birthday . . . for laser tag. Having Mum and Dad there will be bad enough, but watching my grandma play laser tag will give Steve 'bog monitor' even more material for his '*let's humiliate Eddy fun files*'. There must be **SOME** way to save her/me from the humiliation.

'I'll make us a lovely cup of tea,' says Mum.

There's nothing lovely about a cup of tea, but everyone knows that adults have strange tastes in food and beverages.

While Mum's brewing the tea, Grandma goes to use the bathroom, but the floor's still wet from when I mopped and she **SLIPS** over. Even though she's not hurt, she's shaky and has to go and lie down.

'Sorry, Grandma.' I help Mum tuck her into bed.

'It's not your fault, Eddy. Don't worry, I'll be fine.'

I try to be quiet so I don't disturb her while she's resting, so I write down everything I can remember about the book that Rover chewed. I don't have enough money to buy a new copy.

Suddenly, a black shape **STREAKS** past my room. It's Rover in a hurry, cheeks bulging like he has something in his mouth.

I catch him at the back door.

'Rover, give it to me.'

He stares up at me, grinning, showing big teeth.

I copy Dad and put on my **DEEPEST** voice. 'Drop it, Rover.' And he actually does!

I realise that the big teeth aren't his. They belong to **GRANDMA.** Rover was wearing Grandma's false teeth!

I put him outside and take Grandma's teeth to the bathroom to examine them. Apart from being wet and slimy, they look good. For false teeth, I mean. I wash them in hot water, sneak into the spare bedroom and drop them back in the glass next to Grandma's bed.

She must be having a good **DREAM** because she's laughing to herself. I head back to my room. Nobody needs to know about this. I'm pretty sure Rover won't dob.

I'm finally pondering my final book reflection when Mum bursts in. I would have had this homework done ages ago if Mum and Dad didn't keep interrupting me.

'Do you have something to **TELL** me, Eddy?'

How does she know about Grandma's teeth? Who told her? The teeth were fine. Maybe Grandma was foxing and wasn't really asleep when I put them back.

'You **STOLE** from me, Eddy.' Mum has her *'most disappointed'* look on. She holds out her hand with the credit card in it.

Saying that I stole from her is a bit harsh. I was 'borrowing' until my birthday money came through.

'I gave you my card in good faith and you abused my trust.'

'But I bought the book.'

'I would never have given you permission to get that ***Game of Drones*** app. I'd **GROUND** you if you weren't grounded already.'

Am I'm supposed to think that's a **GOOD** thing or not?

'I'll pay you back.' I hope that Grandma comes through with my birthday money.

'It's not about the money. I hate the thought that a computer game is so important to you that you would disrespect me.'

'But I haven't played it for ages.' True because I was grounded and having a police officer for a mum means that I'm under constant surveillance. I have a spark of **INSPIRATION.** 'I did it to help a friend.'

'A friend?'

'Yeah, Macca's guinea pig passed away. Remember I told you that?'

Mum raises an eyebrow.

Macca's guinea pig really did die. 'He was **SHATTERED.** He needed something to distract him. I got it for Macca.'

'His guinea pig?'

'Yeah, its name was **RHUBARB.** He'd had it since it was a kitten.'

'A pup.'

'Na, it was a guinea pig.'

Mum rolls her eyes. 'A baby guinea pig is called a pup, not a kitten.'

So far so good. I've managed to distract her from her suspicions that her eldest son is becoming a hardened **CRIMINAL.** And distracting mums involves a lot of skill.

'I have to admit I've been impressed by the signs of responsibility you've been showing lately, like cleaning your room and the bathroom.' She frowns as if she remembers that's the reason Grandma needs a lie down. 'So I'll give you another chance. But next time I let you have my credit card, don't make me **REGRET** it.'

'I won't. I'm sorry.' I am sorry she found out so fast and that I don't yet have the money to pay her back.

CHAPTER 16:

UNAUTHORISED CREDIT CARD USE

If parents gave us **MORE** pocket money, we'd have less reason for unauthorised credit card expenditure, but they don't seem to have the analytical skills to work that out. Unfortunately for us, they seem to have early **DETECTION** systems when it comes to their credit cards. How does Mum know about the *Game of Drones* app already? I only bought it a couple of days ago.

If you get **CAUGHT** buying essential items with a parent's credit card without permission, try these great tips:

EDDY'S TIPS FOR UNAUTHORISED CREDIT CARD USAGE:

1. Suggest a pocket money raise. If you had enough of your own money you wouldn't need to borrow theirs.
2. Play the sympathy card, but don't use the same story every month. An excuse like your best friend's guinea pig died and you were being a good friend to them will only work once or twice . . . okay three times max (and I'd only try it a third time if Mum and Dad are excessively distracted with other things happening on the home or work front . . . and certainly wouldn't recommend it if either or both of them are police officers.)

SCENARIOS TO ATTRACT SYMPATHY

- You were having a hard time and needed a distraction.
- You're helping a friend in need.
- Your other best friend is having an anxiety attack because the teachers have given you all so much homework – and they needed a distraction.
- The app you bought was a birthday surprise for Mum or Dad.

Okay, so the guinea pig thing didn't actually work and Mum and Dad are making me pay the credit card money **BACK.** They are even making me pay back the cost of the book, which means that I won't be able to afford lettuce for the rabbit next door for six months. (Luckily it seems to be quite happy eating **GRASS.**)

But even without having to buy rabbit food, a guy needs cash for essentials.

To earn extra money, I'll have to wash the car this afternoon. Actually, I'll get **DAVEY** to wash the car and I'll supervise.

DAY 12

WEDNESDAY

It's killing me. Macca and Damo are up to level **SIXTEEN** in ***Game of Drones***. Plus, surf's up and I'm missing it! Damo's latest text came through a second ago. *It's awesome here! When can you hang with us?*

Soon. Hopefully tomoz.

I should be able to get this **LAST** book reflection done by then.

I flick through the half-chewed book. Rover doesn't respect books and reading. Then again, it's better that he demolished my book rather than Grandma's **TEETH.** That would have been seriously awkward. I told Grandma to keep her bedroom door closed from now on. I read the notes I took the other day. I'll have to make up the rest.

Suddenly Dad calls out, 'Eddy, can you give me a hand **RAKING** up grass clippings. Catcher's broken on the mower.'

Why is he even home? Oh yeah, I forgot. He's taken a few days off work to **LOOK AFTER US** so Mum can study for her exam. Not that I need looking after. I'm perfectly fine left to my own devices.

'Eddy, I need help,' Dad calls again.

How is that my problem? Can't he see I'm busy? Probably not, because I have the bedroom door closed. 'I'm doing my book reflections,' I call back.

The door opens. 'Catching up on homework you were supposed to do last term doesn't excuse you from chores,' says Dad.

'Can't Davey help? Why do I have to do **EVERYTHING?'**

'Davey washed the car.'

He does have a point. I scratch my head. How does he even **KNOW** about that?

'Grandma told me. She also says that you pocketed most of the money.'

Thanks, Grandma. I thought Dad would be impressed with my supervisory and delegation skills, but clearly not.

'I think you should give your brother at least

HALF your earnings,' he says.

I'm not entirely happy about that suggestion, but I have managed to distract Dad from the lawn. Unfortunately, it's not for long.

'Come on, Eddy. It should only take ten minutes if we do this together.'

TWO HOURS LATER, I'm finally back at my desk.

I'm about to start my final book reflection when Dad appears in my doorway. Again!

'I think you need a break from the computer,' he says.

'Yeah?' I grin, feeling a **FLUTTER** of excitement. Maybe Dad wants to reward me for this morning's hard work in the garden. I imagine an afternoon at the beach with Macca and Damo.

Then he crushes me. 'You can help with the grocery shopping.'

NOOOOOO!!! 'I'd love to, Dad, but I have to finish my homework.'

'You can't sit at the computer all day. It's bad for you.'

Not as bad as grossery shopping. 'I had a break already, in the garden.'

'I thought you'd jump at the chance to get **OUT** of the house,' says Dad.

Maybe if I show him how helpful I can be, my parents will ease off on the grounding.

I cross my fingers behind my back. 'Sure, Dad. I'd **LOVE** to come.' (About as much as I'd love eating liverwurst sandwiches for breakfast.)

I carry the green bags to the car – and my doom. If I'm going to suffer then it's only **FAIR** my little brother should too, right?

'Is Davey coming?' I ask hopefully. He's not that tall, but he's a formidable shopping-cart racing companion.

Dad shakes his head. 'Davey's at Jen's house.'

Life is so **UNFAIR.** 

CHAPTER 17:

GROSSERY SHOPPING MEANS BORING, NOT BONDING

Did You Know?

A famous child torturer called *Will Suffer* invented shopping. (Well that's my **GUESS** anyway. Seems logical don't you think?)

Taking kids grossery shopping is one of the most **BIZARRE** things parents do. Why would they think we'd want to spend two-and-a-half hours in the supermarket? We could **BUILD** the place in that time.

If you can't get out of grossery shopping, try to make the experience fun. Use this as an **OPPORTUNITY** to convince your parents to leave you at home next time.

My essential tips are bound to help you.

EDDY'S SENSATIONAL SHOPPING ANTIDOTE

Heaps of parents get distracted reading food label ingredients to make sure you're not going to be **POISONED** with chemicals, **CONTAMINATED** with growth hormones or **HYPED** with sugar. This works particularly well if you have an organic-loving parent like my dad. While they're distracted there are lots of things you can do to spice up the shopping experience.

1. Fill the cart with things you would choose to eat, like biscuits and chocolate. This is a great way to show parents your taste in food. They could be closet **CHOCAHOLICS** (this does not mean they eat chocolate in

cupboards), and they might find it too hard to **RESIST** the family chocolate block that you dropped into the cart.

2. If this fails, build a **FORT** out of the toilet roll stack at the end of aisle seven.
3. You could also try convincing your parents how boring shopping is. How do you do that? Find their **WEAK SPOT**. Everyone has a boredom threshold – you have to find it.

FINDING THE BOREDOM THRESHOLD

Sit your parents down for two hours (you might have to **HIDE** their phones) and make them play *Ultimate Maths Invaders*. When they beg you to let them stop playing or fall asleep from boredom, tell them that *Ultimate Maths Invaders* **EQUALS** grossery shopping in your world.

MORE TIPS:
OTHER POSSIBLE REMEDIES FOR BOREDOM IN THE SUPERMARKET
1. Challenge parent to a shopping cart race.
2. Pretend there's a competition going and whoever gets their shopping done quickest, wins a prize.
3. Ask if you can go to the dentist instead of shopping. This should give them a true indication of how much you REALLY HATE GROSSERY SHOPPING!
4. Tell them you've got homework. They'll definitely believe this because thanks to sadistic teachers, you ALWAYS have homework, even on the holidays.

THREE HOURS later, we're back from grossery shopping. What's even more gross is that Dad decided I needed new clothes and his taste in what's cool is at least twenty years out of date. He also bought chips (without food colouring) and chocolate (organic) for my party, which is supposed to be in two days' time. That would be a good thing if my birthday arrangements hadn't become so **COMPLICATED.**

As I drag the last shopping bag inside and dump it on the dining room table, Mum smiles at me. 'Thanks for helping Dad, Eddy. We appreciate it.'

I race to my room, eager to escape the *'putting the shopping away'* ritual and add new chapters to my **PARENT TRAINING GUIDE**. I already have thousands of words of pure **GENIUS** and it hasn't taken that long. Hey, writing a book is easy. Especially when your parents give you so much material to work with.

I'm starting the next chapter when the door opens and Mum hands me a paper bag with Tudor Menswear written on the outside.

'You forgot this,' she says.

'Thanks.' I take the bag from her.

After she leaves, I shove it under my bed while I try to think of a more permanent solution.

CHAPTER 18:

I NEVER ASKED YOU TO BUY ME THAT

Whatever gave Dad the idea I wanted a pair of baggy **GRANDPA** pants? Were my parents born tasteless or did it happen when they got older?

I can't wear those pants. They're not jeans. They don't even have **RIPS** in them. My cool-guy reputation will be shattered. Nobody under the age of **FORTY** wears pants like that.

While those pants are in the house, there's a risk that Mum and Dad will try to make me wear them. This calls for a cunning plan.

Remember, parents are **FRAGILE,** so you need to be sensitive.

Don't blurt out, '*You've got no taste and I wouldn't be seen dead in those daggy pants*', even though it's true. This will send parents warning signals that you don't plan to wear the pants . . . **EVER!**

You could hide the grandpa gear at the back of your cupboard, but there's a danger Dad and Mum will find it when they're doing the spring cleaning, and there's nothing more chilling than the words, 'Oh, look! I found those pants we bought you. Why don't you wear them **NOW?'**

LIONEL WOLF'S STORY: A CASE STUDY

Lionel's parents were like mine – they had terrible taste in names **AND** presents. He'd had the *'Birthday from Hell'* where he'd been given a book on how to improve his **MATH SKILLS** and a pair of baggy pants that Grandpa thought were **TRENDY.**

Lionel had asked for the latest ***BADDIES VS GOODIES*** computer game, so you can imagine how devastated he was with his presents. He was hanging out in the attic coming to terms with his **DISAPPOINTMENT** when he found an old suitcase (but that's not why this story is called a case study). If you hoped there was money inside, I hate to disappoint you.

In the suitcase, Lionel found a bunch of weird clothes that belonged to Dad when **HE** was a kid (Dad's name on the shirt collars was a dead giveaway). Lionel had to get rid of his daggy pants for good so they could never come back to **HAUNT** him – or lie around in an attic for his kids to find. Then he heard his dog Rover barking and now Lionel knew **EXACTLY** what to do.

WHAT TO DO: A PERMANENT SOLUTION

This solution is now called *'Lionel's Theory of Daggy Clothes Disposal'* because he's the one who thought it up. When the dog is having **BREAKFAST,** slip the daggy gear into his kennel. He'll be grateful for something new to rub his tummy on and sharpen his teeth with. By the time you get home from **SCHOOL,** your pants will be ripped to shreds and not able to be worn again. (Clever Lionel!)

FOOTNOTE: If you **DON'T** have a dog or he's on holidays with Grandpa, there's bound to be somebody in the neighbourhood who does.

If all else fails, offer to put the garbage out. It's not your fault if a hideous pair of pants **ACCIDENTALLY** falls into the trash, now, is it?

DAY 13
THURSDAY

For the first time ever, I'm grateful when Dad's shower singing wakes me up before the sun. If I can record my last book reflection straight after breakfast, I should be done by lunchtime. My birthday is **TOMORROW**, which is kind of scary because I'm still grounded, and I still haven't worked out what to do about the laser tag/Steve/Grandma situation. And all it would take is a parental-chore emergency to get me off track from finishing my homework. I have added **INCENTIVE** to finish – the chips and organic chocolate stacked up in the pantry.

I change out of my pyjamas, set the screen and microphone up and begin recording my final reflection.

EDDY POPPENHAGEN'S BOOK REFLECTION №2

GAME ON

JACK, the main character, is twelve like me and he likes computers too. I don't think he's ever played *Game of Drones* before, though, and seeing as he ends up **STRANDED** in the Australian outback with his sister, it looks like he never will.

Jack's mum wins a family holiday of a lifetime, and they can choose to go anywhere. **ANYWHERE!** Disneyland, Movie World, maybe even the moon. But she's an artist and she chooses a **'TECHNOLOGY FREE'** camel trek to the top end of Australia. My parents have some weird ideas too.

Jack ends up in a place where there aren't even any **COMPUTERS,** let alone computer games. But there are snakes and crocodiles and wild pigs.

Feeling sorry for Jack already? You should be.

The camels get a fright and stampede and Mum ends up **INJURED** and Dad goes for help so Jack and his little sister, Flick, end up being left **ALONE** in the wilderness.

Now Jack's like me, **STRANDED.** At least I'm stranded in my room and the kitchen is just a short walk away. No fridge for Jack and Flick, though, and they're running out of food **AND** water.

Jack has to rely on the **VIRTUAL** skills he learned in a computer game *Crocodile Run* to stop him and Flick from starving to death, dying of thirst or being **EATEN** by crocodiles.

If **YOU** want to know whether Jack's computer skills save the day, you'll have to read the book. It's pretty awesome.

Right now, I'm hoping **MY** computer skills will save me from a pretty terrible fate too, being **GROUNDED** on the school holidays.

I'm **FINISHED!** I've completed two book reflections that even Steve **'BOG MONITOR'** would be proud of. I peer at my face in the computer camera and my skin's clear. A double miracle! Monster zits have moved to another galaxy.

I still can't believe that Mum invited Steve to my birthday tomorrow! And she says she loves me? Funny way to show it. Steve will probably **VIDEO** every moment and put it on the blog so everyone will know the minute and boring details of my life.

I have to show Mum by book reflections, otherwise there won't be a birthday! I pick up my laptop and go looking for her. She's sitting at the dining table, reading one of her ultra-thick books, with Rover asleep at her feet. Davey walks towards me, carrying his foam rocket. Grinning, he launches it at me. I hold up my **LAPTOP** to protect myself and it bounces off my screen, landing on Mum's open book.

She jumps, turns and scowls at me. On the other side of her, Davey rolls around on the floor laughing. I can't help **GRINNING** at his reaction.

'Thanks very much,' says Mum. 'You've broken my concentration. These court proceedings are quite complex.'

'I came to show you my book reflections. All done.' I place my laptop in front of her.

She watches each book reflection, but she can't be listening that carefully because she doesn't comment on any references to my **PERSONAL**

CIRCUMSTANCES. She must still be immersed in her own homework. Boring! No wonder Mum seems to forget how to have fun sometimes.

'Great, Eddy. See, that wasn't so hard, was it?' she says.

Not so hard? It was excruciating. 'So, I'm **FREE?**'

She nods. 'Off you go. I'm sure your friends will be pleased to see you. Don't forget to **UPLOAD** your work so Miss McTaggart knows it's done,' says Mum.

'I won't.' I had forgotten.

Davey grabs his rocket and follows me out. 'Where are you going?'

'To the beach.' I message the guys telling them I'll be there by twelve o'clock.

Davey runs after me. 'Will you play rockets first?'

I don't want to be mean, but I'm **LATE** already. 'Sorry, mate. Next time, I promise.'

'But I'm bored,' he says. 'Jen's not coming over for another hour.'

I have a plan for how he could fill in some time. 'Hey, Davey, do you want to do a job for me? I'll give you **FOUR** dollars.'

'Really?'

I take the money from my pocket. It's the other part of the car-wash money that Dad said I had to pay **HIM.**

'What do I have to do?'

I hand him my laptop. 'Could you upload my reflections to my class server? My username is ***Eddy Popcorn*** and password is ***ROVER*** and my birth date.

'Okay.'

'Thanks, Davey. I owe you. Just put the laptop

back on my desk when you finish.' I hand him the four dollars and he grins at me as if I handed him four **HUNDRED.**

'Thanks, Eddy. I'll do it now.'

'Great. See you when I get back from the beach.'

I bolt out the door. I haven't hung out with my mates in ages . . . and we have waves to catch.

Macca and Damo have built an amazing **FORT** out of driftwood on the beach. I wish I'd been there for the construction phase.

'You should have seen us dragging that piece up from the water's edge.' Macca points to the biggest log.

'This is so **COOL.**' I walk

around the fort. It's almost as big as my bedroom. 'Nice job, guys.'

'How does freedom taste?' asks Damo.

'Almost as good as Crispy Cones' blueberry crunch.'

'Yeah . . . and perfect timing. **ICE-CREAM** lady's here.' Macca points to the rainbow-painted caravan pulled up on the foreshore.

We race across the sand. Rule is, last one there buys the cones.

This time it's Macca, but he doesn't seem to care. 'I got a pocket money raise,' he says.

Course he did! **EVERYONE** seems to get a raise but me.

We sit in the shelter of the fort eating our ice-creams. Macca and Damo have gone for double choc. 'Still reckon **BLUEBERRY'S** the best.' I lick purple drips off my hand.

'Are you looking forward to your birthday, Popsicle?' asks Macca. 'You do know it's tomorrow?'

'Of course.'

'Is laser tag back on then?' asks Damo.

I can't lie to a mate to their face. 'Yeah.'

'Way to go!' says Damo.

Yeah, **AWESOME!**

I get home just before dark and Mum greets me with a potentially 'appetite spoiling' chocolate milkshake and walnut cookies.

'What's happened? Is it Grandma?' This isn't **NORMAL** Mum behaviour.

Mum shakes her head. 'Grandma's fine. It's about your birthday tomorrow.'

'What about it?'

'I had a call from the laser-tag owners. The popcorn machine caught fire and burnt half the place down so they've had to **CLOSE** it temporarily for repairs.'

Popcorn machine! Ironic! I knew laser tag was doomed, ever since Mum invited Steve. It's like he **JINXED** the whole thing. On the other hand, this could save a lot of embarrassment all round. I think fast. It's a good time to take advantage of the fact that Mum clearly feels bad for me.

'I guess we'll have a gathering here then, before the sleepover. You and Dad could go out for the night.' Now the laser tag is off, Steve might **CANCEL** too.

'I'm not leaving you home alone, Eddy. You're too young.'

'I'm **ALMOST** twelve.'

'Not till ten o'clock at night,' she says.

'Close enough.'

'Still not old enough.' Dad, of course, takes Mum's side.

'Grandma will be here.' I say this knowing she's usually asleep by **7.00 PM.**

This can't be happening. After all that I've just gone through – grounded for most of the holidays – and now my birthday is going to be a complete dud.

'Steve's thirteen already,' I say desperately. He acts old, so he probably is.

'Hmm, he is a very responsible young man,' says Mum.

'Please?' I can't believe Steve **'BOG MONITOR'** might actually save the day.

Mum pauses. 'There's a new action comedy at the cinema that I'd like to see. Are you sure you don't want us to be here, though? It is your birthday.'

'It's fine, Mum. You should go.'

'They won't have Davey to look after,' says Dad. 'He's going to Jen's after lunch.'

Mum nods. 'And Grandma will be here.'

'I want you to have a good time too,' I say. Parents **LOVE** it when you think of someone 'other than yourself'.

'Oh, okay then. But don't let us down, Eddy,' says Mum.

'WE WON'T.'

DAY 14 FRIDAY

Birthday

My twelfth birthday starts full of promise. It's still the holidays (just) and I'm not grounded! I leap out of bed and land in a pile of Rover's **VOMIT.** Guess those walnut cookies I shared yesterday didn't agree with him.

Davey races in with my birthday present. He saved his pocket money and bought me a cool **LAPTOP CASE.** Wish I'd given him more cash for cleaning the car. Maybe next time. He also offers to remove Rover's unpleasant

birthday gift. 'Thanks, Davey.' Best birthday present ever.

Mum and Dad give me new lights for my bike, which is totally cool because it means I can stay **LATER** at the beach and come back after dark. 'As long as you're careful and stick to the bike paths,' says Mum.

'I will.'

Grandma's present is last and I'm sweating on it. I haven't forgotten that I **OWE** Mum money.

'Happy Birthday, my big grandson. I have a surprise for you.' She plants a sloppy kiss on my cheek and from behind her back she pulls out a **TUDOR MENSWEAR** bag. Inside is a brown pair of grandpa pants and a green shirt to match, only it doesn't match at all.

'Thanks, Gran.' I hug her, trying to hide my disappointment. How will I pay Mum back now? Rover nudges the bag with his nose. I open it so he can

have a sniff and he wags his tail. At least he looks happy.

After lunch, Davey heads off to Jen's and the guys arrive. Macca has the **BIGGEST** chocolate block ever for me and Damo's presents are a wax comb to clean my board and a cool beach towel.

Steve hands me an envelope. It's probably a book voucher (as if I haven't read enough books lately). But inside the card is **$30** cash. Awesome! And unexpected! I can pay off my debts now. I hate owing Mum money.

'Thanks, guys. These presents are the best.'

'Happy Birthday, Ed,' says Steve. 'You get your **HOMEWORK** done?' He grins.

I grin back. 'Yep, all finished.' I ignore the 'Ed'. I hate it when people call me that, but I'm still hyped about his present.

'Bet your parents were impressed,' Steve's grin widens.

'Yeah. I guess.' Funny thing for **HIM** to say. Not for the first time, I wonder if Steve is actually a parent in disguise. But for now, I plan to focus on the fact that today I turn **TWELVE** and I'm working my way towards adulthood which I hope will bring me way more rights than I have now.

Macca and Damo have brought their gaming equipment so we can play ***Game of Drones.***

It's Steve and I versus Damo and Macca. I didn't feel **RIGHT** putting one of them on a team with Steve seeing as he's really Mum's friend not mine. But he acts more like a kid when he's playing ***Game of Drones.*** He almost swears, though you can't really call 'bummer' a swearword.

We eat the awesome party food that Dad

serves up (no liverwurst sandwiches today) and I contemplate the long, fun night ahead.

But after we've eaten, Mum interrupts my joyful anticipation with a disappointing announcement. 'Grandma's not feeling well so we've decided to stay **HOME** tonight.'

'You're **KIDDING**, right?'

Grandma does look a bit pale.

'I'm afraid not. I think I'll go for a lie down,' Grandma says.

'We can look after her,' I say.

Mum smiles. 'That's kind, Eddy, but we'd worry about her, and I don't want anything to **SPOIL** your birthday.'

Mum and Dad staying home is the thing most likely to spoil my birthday, apart from Steve '**BOG MONITOR**' being there. (Although he does seem to be putting in some effort).

'Don't worry, Eddy,' says Dad. 'It'll be fine.'

It's a **NIGHTMARE**, but I can see that nothing is going to change their minds.

'I hope you're feeling better soon, Grandma. Make sure you close your door,' I remind her. Rover stealing Grandma's teeth is all I need.

'Aren't you lucky that we get to spend the night with you after all?' says Mum.

'LUCKY' is not the word I would have used! But because I'm a kind, tactful and thoughtful son who doesn't like to hurt my mother's feelings, I force a smile. 'It's great, Mum.'

The thought of Mum and Dad being here all night is enough to put me off my chocolate **LOG-TRAIN** birthday cake.

Steve snorts when he sees it. 'Jen had one of those for her birthday last year,' he says.

Thanks for the reminder that Mum made me the **SAME** cake for my six-year-old birthday party. It tastes good though.

Mum gets takeaway pizza for tea, then there's the part I've been dreading – afterwards. Parents can be a real downer at sleepovers.

'We should organise a SINGSTAR competition,' Mum suggests.

Is she serious? It's going to be bad enough that my mates will see Mum in her pyjamas. Her singing on top of that is too much to bear.

PARENTS IN PYJAMAS

How **EMBARRASSING!** (Need I say more?)

It's bad enough that Dad has knobby knees and hairy legs like a gorilla, but does he have to show the **WORLD,** wandering around the house in his shorty pyjamas? He even goes out the front in them to take the bins out. **MORTIFYING.**

At least Mum covers up. But seriously, a **TEDDY BEAR** dressing-gown? And let's not talk about her hippopotamus pyjamas and **FLUFFY** slippers. Why do mums think it's cute to walk around wearing fluffy rabbits on their feet? I stopped wearing mine when I was **FIVE.** Too embarrassing!

To avoid your cooler-than-the-North-Pole mates seeing your mum and dad in their **DORKY** sleepwear, you'll have to take drastic measures.

HOW MANY WAYS CAN PARENTS IN PYJAMAS BE EMBARRASSING?

EDDY'S PRACTICAL PARENTS IN PYJAMAS ANTIDOTE

Here are some options to consider:

1. **DON'T** have sleepovers. (As if that's an option? You can't ban sleepovers! The gang will think there's something weird going on at your house. Then again, they'll know there **IS** something weird going on at your house if they come for a sleepover.)
2. Go to your room to escape the situation and write **HELP** on your window. Hopefully, someone will come to your aid (like **I** have with this book). It could be a police officer, and that will inspire Mum and Dad to change out of their **RIDICULOUS** clothes pronto, especially if it's someone they know.
3. Buy a rabbit (if you're like me and don't have one already), get a hutch and hope that Mum won't notice her fluffy bunny slippers **CAMOUFLAGED** in there.
4. There's nothing else for it. You'll have to spend your hard-earned money buying Mum

and Dad **DECENT** sleepwear. Everyone knows that parents can't resist wearing presents that their kids buy for them. It's an opportunity to show off. 'Look how kind, unselfish and wonderful my child is. He/she bought me this **FABULOUS** present.' They won't be able to resist modelling the sleepwear at your next sleepover.

It's not just the pyjama thing. Parents can find **SO MANY** ways to be weird and embarrassing when you have friends over – it's their **SPECIAL** skill. Believe me.

After we decline the offer of **SINGSTAR**, Mum takes it upon **HERSELF** to provide the musical entertainment. It's my worst nightmare – the thing I'd hoped we would avoid by not having karaoke. No offence, but Mum's voice sounds like a cross between a starving goat and a cat being swung by its tail and she thinks she's **BEYONCÉ**. It gets worse when she decides to do a dance challenge and drags Dad with her onto the newly polished floor in front of my friends.

We all end up **DEAD.** I die of embarrassment, my friends die laughing and my parents die from fatal injuries. Thankfully Grandma was in bed so she wasn't involved in the fiasco.

Mum isn't actually dead. She suffered concussion from where she slipped on the polished floorboards and hit her **HEAD.** Dad isn't dead either, but he panicked about Mum and almost hyperventilated after he called the paramedics. Even they get to see Mum in her rabbit slippers and hippopotamus pyjamas. They check Mum and Dad out and assure us they'll make a full recovery. I'm not sure I will.

In a flash of optimism, I consider the fact that this whole experience might be a good thing – it might put an end to Mum's Beyoncé impersonations.

CHAPTER 20:

SHOW-OFF PARENTS SHOULDN'T PERFORM IN PUBLIC

According to 'experts', parents feel public performances are **NECESSARY** not just because they want to showcase their talents. Experts say that clapping is therapeutic for parents. They like applause, even if it's their **OWN.** And they definitely like attention, even if it's the **MEDICAL** kind.

Why does having friends over seem to put mums in a **PERFORMING** mood? It's not easy to explain this phenomenon, except that your mum, like mine, probably missed out on the lead role in the school musical and has **NEVER** got over the fact that she didn't get her big star moment in front of an audience.

Here are my **AMAZING** tips on how to handle this traumatic situation.

EDDY'S SUPERB SHOW-OFF PARENTS ANTIDOTE

1. **LOCK** you and your friends in your room. There, you can play your **OWN** music on high volume to drown Mum out, but this might not work if she is determined and bitter about the lost opportunity when she was your age. In that case, keep five pairs of **EARPLUGS** handy.
2. You might also consider buying SingStar and asking the neighbours **EIGHT** doors down if they'd mind setting it up in their **SOUNDPROOF** concrete garage so Mum can practice her singing there. You may have to mow the neighbour's lawns **DAILY** in exchange

for such a huge favour, but it's a small price to pay.

3. Spreading **HONEY** or lemonade on the floor is good for stopping parents from trying to perform complex dance routines – although it can lead to **CONCUSSION**.
4. Sometimes parents even state that they are using this opportunity to show you how demanding and embarrassing **YOU** can be. (As if?)
5. Try to see their terrible singing in a **POSITIVE** way. After all, their voice can't be **THAT** bad, can it? (**IGNORE** this antidote. It was obviously thought up by an adult.)

DAY 15
SATURDAY

After breakfast, it's time for my twelfth birthday party to **END.** Mum hands out special lolly bags to all the guys. Despite what the ambulance officers said, the concussion must have seriously affected Mum's brain. I haven't had lolly bags at a party since I was eight! Macca and Damo are cool about it, but Steve almost **CHOKES** on his orange juice.

Steve's mum comes to pick him up and she drops Davey off at the same time. He's pretty rapt with the lolly bags, even if I'm not.

After everyone leaves, Grandma helps Mum change the dressing on her head **BUMP** and Mum goes off to do her 'million and one things'. Dad hovers around for a while and then disappears to his study to check his emails.

FINALLY, the house is quiet – no sign of Mum or Dad. I can hear Davey humming in his bedroom next to mine. Now's my chance.

I tuck Grandma's Tudor Menswear present under my arm and slink out to Rover's kennel. **BUMMER.** Mum's hanging out the washing. I quickly shove the bag behind a bush.

'Hey, Mum, shouldn't you be resting your concussion? I can do that for you,' I offer.

She looks at me as if I'm an alien. 'Do you even know how to hang up washing?' she asks.

I'm **DEEPLY** wounded. 'Of course I do.' How hard can it be?

'Okay. Thanks. I appreciate it.' She hugs me and strolls back to the house.

I pick up a wet shirt from the basket. I throw it over the line and peg it down. Looks like the way Mum did it – well **ALMOST.** I glance around – nobody's watching. Finally.

I creep over to the bush and grab the Tudor Menswear bag. Rover jumps up and down, yapping excitedly, as I push the contents of the bag into his kennel. He sure seems grateful for his new

BLANKET, but I wish he wouldn't tell everyone about it. Rover's great the way he's happy to share my presents.

Later, Grandma heads off in a taxi. She'll be back in six months for Davey's birthday. Rover should be due for **NEW** kennel blankets by then.

It's so awesome not being grounded anymore. Should be enough time for me to play a round of ***Game of Drones*** with Davey before I head to the beach for my first proper surf of the holidays.

DAY 16
SUNDAY

It's the last day of the holidays . . . **SOB.** But at least I get to spend the whole day with my mates. Of course I invite Davey and Rover too because I can't leave them stranded at home with Mum and Dad on our **LAST** day of freedom.

Mum stops us as we're heading out the door and pulls a $50 note out of her purse and hands it to me. 'Get yourselves something yummy for lunch. My treat. And don't forget hats and sunscreen.'

'Thanks, Mum. Are you feeling okay?'

'I'm fine.'

The sun is **SMILING** on us as we race into the street.

Damo and Macca are already at the beach. Sun's out, waves are rolling and I'm back with my mates. Doesn't get much better than **THIS.** The day is full of awesome. Nobody mentions the fact that our freedom ends tomorrow or that I just got mine back. We're living the moment.

We surf all morning, then eat fish and chips, sitting on our towels. Rover has been digging a moat at the edge of the water and he flops onto the sand next to us. The fish and chips are

SO good. Way better than sandwiches. They must be called sandwiches because they end up with sand in them at the beach, so when you bite down you get a mouthful of grit. Gross. Yep, fish and chips is the perfect beach lunch.

We arrive home wet, covered in sand and **HAPPY**, but it doesn't take long for Mum and Dad to spoil our great mood. Mum must be feeling better. 'You should get an early night. School tomorrow,' she says.

We spent all day trying to forget about that.

At eight o'clock Dad says, 'School night. Time for bed.'

It's **NOT** a school night. It's the last day of the holidays. Does he have to make things worse?

I'm not ready to sleep yet so I add my recap, recommended reading and glossary to my **PARENT TRAINING GUIDE**.

REMEDY RECAP:

In *EDDY POPCORN'S GUIDE TO PARENT TRAINING* I've tried to cover as many scenarios as possible and provide mostly practical, effective suggestions. But parents are clever at finding new ways to be weird, difficult and embarrassing.

So, if your parent problem or training trauma isn't included here, don't sue me. Send me a polite letter and I'll try and include it in my sequel.

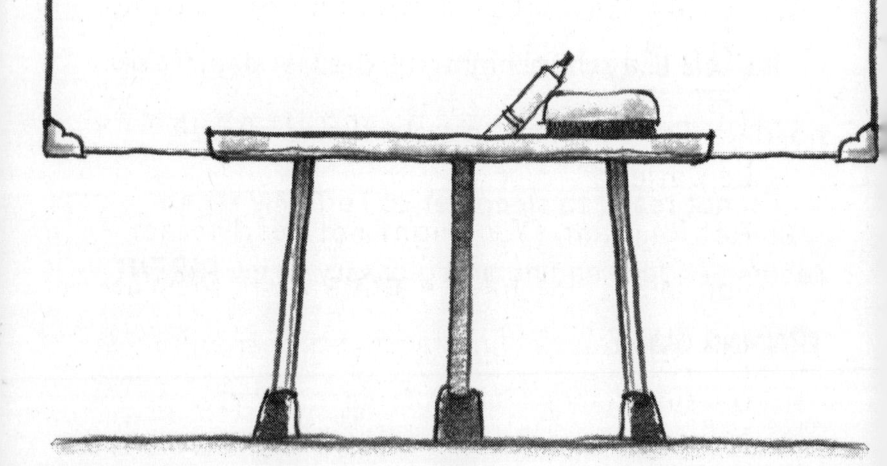

IT'S UP TO YOU!

It's true that parents can frustrate, humiliate and annoy (without even trying). But you can make a **DIFFERENCE!**

I'm not sure **HOW** yet, but when I find out I'll let you know.

THIS BOOK IS YOUR SECRET WEAPON

In the meantime, you might like to try some of the solutions I suggested. In case you have a mind like a **SOGGY** tomato sandwich, here's a recap of the major weapons you have at your disposal.

1. Be **CONSISTENTLY** distracting or annoying. (This may come naturally to you already.) This is good for parents and trains them to be patient.
2. Act ignorant. (You might not need to act – you might not have a **CLUE** what they are talking about.) This clever response will train parents to communicate more clearly.

3. Play the **EMPATHY** card. (That's where Mum and Dad get to 'feel' what you're going through.)
4. Feed unwanted food, clothing or other **ACCESSORIES** to the dog or cat, or the next door neighbour's dog or cat. (No training involved here, but if it means side stepping angry teachers and avoiding eating lamb's **LIVER** or cow's **KIDNEYS,** I think you'll agree that's a good thing. Especially for the lamb and the cow. Okay, maybe not for them because it will be too **LATE,** they'll already have been served up . . . but your stomach will **DEFINITELY** thank you for applying this technique.)
5. Be creative. (I'm not exactly sure what that means but you **MIGHT** be able to figure it out.)
6. **HIDE.** (You've probably practised this form of avoidance for a while already.) This will train your parents to hone their **SEARCH** and **DISCOVER** skills.
7. Get parents involved. What! **NO WAY!** (Oh, hang on . . . ***I*** suggested that!)

8. Argue, plead or do whatever works for you.
9. Call '**1300-MY-PARENTS-ARE-WEIRD-AND EMBARRASSING**'. (Don't call me. I have nothing more to offer. I have generously shared all my wisdom in this book. So show some **GRATITUDE**.)

GOOD LUCK and if all else fails, you might need to grow up and **LEAVE** home.

ACKNOWLEDGEMENTS

I would like to thank 'at least' two people and the **PARROT** I interviewed for their help in writing this guide. No animals were tested in my research (well, the parrot was, but he passed with flying colours). Also, **APOLOGIES** to any rabbits mentioned in this book – no offence intended. I like rabbits.

SUGGESTED READING

If you want to read **MORE** about this topic, too bad! I haven't written any other books – yet.

And seeing as the next school term is about to start and we'll probably have a stack of homework from **DAY ONE**, you'll have to wait a while for the sequel. (But I'm sure it will be worth it.)

While you're waiting, you might like to take the opportunity to write a **FIVE-STAR** review of EDDY POPCORN'S GUIDE TO PARENT TRAINING.

In the meantime, here are some **OTHER** guides and books you might want to check out (or not).

I Don't Want to Be a Mushroom Scientist
by **I C FUNGHI**

How to Get a Pocket Money Raise
by **CON MANN**

Don't Come in My Room
by **LOCKIE DAW**

How to Fit More in Your Bedroom
by **EVA BOX**

How to Fix Show-Off Parents
by **BEA RUTH LESS**

How to Take Charge of the Remote Control
by **JUSTIN TIME**

Improve Your Report Card
by **R U KIDDING**

Why Music Must be Loud
by **R U DEF**

Coincidentally, these titles are all published by **FAY KERR BOOKS.**

GLOSSARY

BIRTHDAY: That day of the year parents get to humiliate their kids in front of **ALL** their friends at once.

CLASS BLOG/BOG: Web page or website set up to help parents **SPY** on their kids and result in their maximum **HUMILIATION.**

DOG: A four-legged garbage disposal unit. Some animals in the species can devour grandpa pants or half a book in a **SINGLE** swallow. Here's a tip – **SOME** of them also eat liverwurst sandwiches.

FISHPOND: Waterhole where books go to drink.

GARAGE: Place where parents store engagement and wedding presents they never **OPENED** from people they never **LIKED.** Smelly organic garden products and mushroom kits are also stored here as well as broken **ELECTRICAL** items that Mum and Dad have been 'meaning to fix' or 'repurpose'.

GROSSERY SHOPPING: A game invented to **TORTURE** kids.

GUFFAW: A type of laugh or tactless action by parents when something **EMBARRASSING** happens to their kids.

LIVERWURST SANDWICHES: Derived their name from the fact that they are the worst-tasting sandwiches **EVER.**

NFP: Not For Parents.

NUTS: Not Unlike Tomato Sandwiches (parenting experts fall into this category).

Mum knocks on my door and it opens. 'Eddy, why are you still up? **LIGHTS OUT!'**

'Yes, Mum.'

She looks at me. 'You got that homework done in the end.'

I nod.

'Proud of you.' She smiles.

After she leaves, I read back through ***EDDY POPCORN'S GUIDE TO PARENT TRAINING.*** I'm pretty **PROUD** of me too.

DAY 1
MONDAY
(FIRST DAY BACK AT SCHOOL)

As soon as I step on the bus, it feels like all the kids are **LOOKING** at me.

'Why is everyone staring at us?' whispers Davey.

Huh, so it wasn't my imagination. 'I don't know.' It's weird!

Steve's in the seat behind the driver and he **BURSTS** out laughing when we walk past. Then he turns and looks out the window as if he doesn't want us to realise that he thinks we're hilarious.

At first I think someone must have stuck a sign saying something stupid on my back. I feel behind me. Nothing there. As I walk down the aisle, kids yell out stuff like, 'Way to go, Popcorn' and **'GREAT TIPS'.**

Mandy McCrae, who hasn't spoken to me since I accidentally jammed her braid in the classroom door in grade two, **HIGH-FIVES** me. 'You're a legend, Popcorn.'

'I am?'

'Yeah! Read your blog post. It was awesome.'

Blog post? Major weird! I didn't post anything. And no kid willingly reads the class blog, ever. I'm starting to feel **UNEASY.**

'Yeah, that chapter about messy rooms was a fave. Can so relate. You should see what my parents keep in their garage, and they hassle me about mess.'

What!? Where did she see that chapter?

Brian Hayes says, 'Your **PARENT TRAINING GUIDE** is so funny. Wish I'd thought of it myself.'

UH-OH!

I feel sick. This can't be happening. I turn to Davey. My voice shakes. 'What did you upload to my class server?'

Davey goes bright red. 'I'm sorry Eddy, really I am. I forgot to do it earlier. I was so excited about the four dollars.'

I look at him, not quite getting it yet.

'But I uploaded it last night, before the end of the holidays,' Davey explains. 'It'll get to Miss McTaggart in time. I mean, school hasn't started yet – we're still on the bus!'

I blink at him, realising that he if uploaded it last night that meant he snuck into my room when I was asleep, but that's not what's important right now.

'Davey,' I ask, slowly, 'WHAT file did you upload?'

He shrugs. 'The file that you asked me to. ***Eddy's Real Reflections***.'

'Oh no! Davey! That's the **WRONG** one!' And somehow the upload found its way from the class share folder to the blog. I don't think that was an accident. Steve **'BOG MONITOR'** is clearly not my friend, after all. No wonder he was laughing. He knows how much **TROUBLE** I'll be in.

Davey screws up his face. 'Wasn't ***Eddy's Real***

Reflections the file you said?'

I try to stay calm. 'No, it was ***Eddy's Reflections***.'

'I'm sorry.' Davey's bottom lip trembles.

'Don't worry, buddy. It's not your fault.' As **ANNOYED** as I am right now, this isn't Davey's fault. I shouldn't have called my masterpiece ***Eddy's Real Reflections***, even though it seemed like a good idea at the time. I was worried if Mum and Dad checked my computer and saw **EDDY POPCORN'S GUIDE TO PARENT TRAINING**, they would go **BALLISTIC.**

I try to breathe, reassure myself that the situation is not as bad as it seems. Nobody reads the blog, remember? Problem with that theory is that clearly kids do read it. And that means potentially teachers and **PARENTS** too. Including mine!

'It's a masterpiece, Popcorn.' Mandy McCrae flops down in the seat across the aisle. 'That ending is so cool. I need to buy a copy.' She laughs. 'Don't tell

Mum and Dad I'm buying it though.'

'You know about my **PARENT TRAINING GUIDE**?'

She gestures around the bus. 'Everyone does!'

I can't believe this is happening.

I am so **DEAD.**

ABOUT THE AUTHOR

Like Eddy Popcorn, Dee would rather create her own books than write about other people's. She has never been a twelve-year-old boy, but she had two of them living in her house . . . and two rabbits. She grew up with the most embarrassing parents ever, although her sons may disagree and she always hated grossery shopping and liverwurst sandwiches, which she believes should only be fed to dogs. Unfortunately when Dee was twelve there was no freecall 1300-MY-PARENTS-ARE-WEIRD-AND EMBARRASSING, and there still isn't, which is why she and Eddy wrote this important book.

ABOUT THE ILLUSTRATOR

Benjamin Johnston works as a mild-mannered architect by daytime but roams imaginary streets as a masked vigilante-illustrator by night (with a cape . . . OK, no, not with a cape). Add to this that he is also a husband and dad of two girls, and he is really looking forward to the day he might actually have enough time for everything he wants to get done. Drawing and illustrating for children have always been his passion. In doing the illustrations for Eddy Popcorn, he basically modelled Eddy's dad on himself (Yes . . . he is that daggy). Benjamin lives and works in Sydney and probably always will. Although Norway sounds nice.

ACKNOWLEDGEMENTS

To Nick and Sam who inspired Eddy, Cill who provided some essential research information, Peter who doesn't know he's in this book, and to all the rabbits I have ever known.

Thanks also to my amazing publisher, Clare Halifax who connected with Eddy right from the start, my wonderful editor Kristy Bushnell who always makes me a better writer and the team at Scholastic Australia who clearly understand that kids need self-help guides as much as they need joke books.

And Ben Johnston, illustrator, who is mind-blowingly talented! You saw inside my brain and drew Eddy exactly like I pictured him.